PELICAN BOOKS A601

Wildlife in Britain

RICHARD FITTER

Wildlife in Britain

RICHARD FITTER

With sixty-seven illustrations

PENGUIN BOOKS

*in conjunction and collaboration with
the Council for Nature*

Penguin Books Ltd, Harmondsworth, Middlesex
U.S.A.: Penguin Books Inc., 3300 Clipper Mill Road, Baltimore 11, Md
AUSTRALIA: Penguin Books Pty Ltd, 762 Whitehorse Road, Mitcham, Victoria

First published 1963
Copyright © Council for Nature, 1963

Made and printed in Great Britain by Jarrold & Sons Ltd, Norwich
Set in Monotype Plantin

Contents

Acknowledgements

The Council for Nature and the author are grateful to those who have read all or part of the manuscript and proofs at various stages, or have supplied information. Especial thanks are due to Dr Francis Rose, Chairman of the Kent Naturalists' Trust, who is responsible for the part of Chapter 2 on the lower plants, and to Mr J. H. P. Sankey, Warden of Juniper Hall Field Centre, who has written the section of Chapter 3 dealing with the invertebrates. Mr Eric Hosking, Mr John Clegg, Professor G. Manley, and Mr A. G. Bourne have kindly supplied paragraphs, Miss B. Davies of the Council's Intelligence Unit prepared the Appendix, and Miss S. Kenyon of the Intelligence Unit carried out the research on which some of the statistical information about societies is based. Mr J. E. Lousley and Mrs M. S. Fitter, with Mr D. J. B. Copp and other members of the Council's staff, have read the manuscript and proofs. Small sections have been kindly checked and commented on by Mr P. E. Brown, Mr C. P. Castell, Mr John Clegg, Professor Gordon Manley, Mr F. J. Taylor Page, and Mr A. E. Smith.

We are also particularly indebted to the Nature Conservancy for their kind cooperation in permitting us to select the great majority of the photographs of animals and plants from the National Collection of Nature Photographs, which is in their care. Acknowledgements for the use of individual figures are as follows:

To W. R. Bawden, Eagle Photos (Fig. 62); Botanical Society of the British Isles and Thomas Nelson & Sons Ltd (Figs. 52–3, taken from their publication *Atlas of the British Flora*); John Clegg (Fig. 54); Ben Darby (Fig. 60); Element (Sound & Sight) Ltd (Figs. 64–5); Crown copyright Farndale (Fig. 63); J. A. Fitton, A.R.P.S. (Figs. 10, 37, and 43); R. H. Hall (Figs. 8, 13, and 46); D. Hatton (Fig. 6); H. A. Hems (Fig. 17); Thomas Henshall,

ACKNOWLEDGEMENTS

A.R.P.S. (Figs. 2 and 39); Walter E. Higham, F.R.P.S., F.I.B.P. (Figs. 19 and 47); Eric Hosking, F.R.P.S. (Figs. 16, 18, 44, 50, 58, and 66–7 as well as Figs. 22 and 41: photos by A. R. Thompson); D. A. J. Hunford (Fig. 56); Anne Jackson (Figs. 9, 11, 42, and 49); G. B. Kearey (Fig. 45); John Leng & Co. (Fig. 61: photo by Robert M. Adam); John Markham (Figs. 5, 7, 14–15, 20–1, 38, 40, and 57); Professor H. W. Miles (Fig. 34); R. K. Murton (Fig. 12); National Museum of Wales (Fig. 55: photo by Arthur Brook); Nature Conservancy (Fig. 59); Rothamsted Experimental Station (Fig. 4); John Sankey (Figs. 23–30, 33, and 35); Scottish Tourist Office (Fig. 3); Dr Stuart G. Smith (Fig. 48); South Bedfordshire News Agency (Fig. 51); A. Faulkner Taylor, F.I.B.P., F.R.P.S. (Fig. 36); D. C. Thomson & Co Ltd (Fig. 1); J. A. Wilson (Fig. 32); Gordon F. Woods, F.R.P.S., F.R.E.S. (Figs. 31a and b).

1 Introductory: The Physical Setting

It is no accident that interest in natural history and wildlife has been strong in Britain for three hundred years or more. The British Isles, an archipelago in the shallow seas of the Continental shelf off the Earth's largest land mass, have as variable a climate and as varied a geology as anywhere in the world, and these two factors have produced a remarkable range of habitats for animals and plants, terrestrial, freshwater, and marine. In some districts, for instance, plants that are common in the Arctic grow to the southward of others that are more generally associated with the Mediterranean, while birds from breeding grounds as far from each other as Greenland and Arctic Russia may spend the autumn or winter in Britain in adjacent flocks.

With this rich raw material to hand, it is not surprising that the Renaissance, and the rise of science in the seventeenth century, combined to produce a tradition of amateur interest in geology and wildlife that is still vigorous and strong. It is this tradition that this book sets out to record, by describing first, very briefly, the range of wildlife to be seen in the British Isles against its physical background and in its various habitats, and then the naturalists themselves, what they are doing, and how they do it. Ireland and the Isle of Man are included in the scope of the book, but the Channel Isles, which are geographically more closely associated with Europe, are not.

In determining the kinds of animal and plant that are found in the British Isles, and their relative frequency, three main factors override all others: the climate; the soil, which derives from the underlying rocks; and the activities of man, which in the past two thousand or so years have substantially changed the relative abundance of many animals and plants in Britain, and have also introduced many kinds of wildlife that might never have made their way here by natural means.

THE CLIMATE

One has only to reflect how different is the climate of New York, with its harshly cold winters and oppressively hot summers, from the much abused but much pleasanter climate of London, a full ten degrees farther north, to realize how powerful an influence the warm water of the Atlantic Ocean has on the climate of the British Isles and thus on the kinds of animal and plant that can live in them. This warmth derives from the overwhelmingly preponderant flow of air from westerly directions. This air, in turn, has travelled over a sea which is unusually warm for its latitude, thanks to the prevailing drift of the surface waters from more southerly regions, the so-called North Atlantic Drift. In winter the British seas are entirely free of ice, in contrast to the waters off the North American continent in the same latitude; throughout the year, indeed, our seas are about 15°F. (8°C.) warmer than those lying off Labrador. Yet the northernmost part of the British Isles, Unst in the Shetlands, is almost as near the Arctic Circle as the southernmost part of Baffin Island. This nearness to the sources of colder air in the Polar regions interacts with the prevailing flow of warm air and warm water from the westward to make the British Isles a constant battleground for opposing weather systems, and the animals and plants that succeed in colonizing them must be able to adapt themselves to a wide range of temperature, rainfall, and sunshine.

It is this constant alternation of masses of warm and cold air over the British Isles that makes our climate so variable and so convenient a stand-by in conversation. For most of the year westerly winds are bringing moist and fairly warm air in from the Atlantic. This air has often originated in the Polar regions, but has been warmed up as it passed across the North Atlantic Drift. To the fact that these westerly winds blow most steadily from November to February we owe our relatively mild winters, averaging in January from 38°F. (3°C.) in eastern England and Scotland to 45°F. (7°C.) in south-western Ireland.

This prevalent type of weather, however, is often interrupted by incursions of other types of air, either warm tropical or sub-tropical air from the region around the Azores or even from Africa, or very cold air from Siberia or the Arctic. This produces marked fluctuations of temperature over a short time, and means that even the far north of Scotland may have its subtropical moments in summer, while the favoured Cornish Riviera and Isles of Scilly may on rare occasions languish under snow and biting north-easterly winds in winter. Even more disconcerting, there can be unseasonably warm spells in winter and cold ones in summer.

Broadly speaking, the east and north of the British Isles are cooler than the south and west, while the west is wetter than the east. Thus in broad terms the south-east tends to be dry and cool in winter but warm in summer; the south-west warmer and wetter; the north-west cool and wet; and the north-east cool and dry. But there are many local climatic variations that tone down this broad picture. The bottom of a Chiltern valley near Rickmansworth, for instance, has a winter climate that for intensity of frost has been compared with that of the upland Aberdeenshire valleys in the coolest inhabited part of Britain; while many subtropical plants are able to grow in the open in the sheltered gardens at Inverewe in Wester Ross (Fig. 1), which is in the same latitude as Ungava Bay in northern Labrador.

Fluctuations in winter temperature and in summer temperature and sunshine are among the most important factors affecting the distribution of animals and plants in Britain. Many are controlled by their inability to stand winter frosts (or even spring frosts, for the occasional severe May frosts are probably even more damaging) or on the other hand by the fact that our summers are rarely warm enough to ripen their fruits or hatch their eggs. With trees and shrubs the average warmth of the period when they are laying down the flowering shoots of the coming year may be of vital importance, and it seems likely, for instance, that the irregular flowering of the beech in Britain

and its restriction as a native tree to the southern part of Britain may be due to a combination of these causes. It was noticeable too that the prodigious flowering of the hawthorn in May 1960 followed on the extremely fine warm summer of 1959, whereas after the dismal wet summer of 1960 there was an almost complete failure of the haw crop in the autumn of 1961.

One of the crucial points for vegetation in Britain is the time in the early spring when the mean temperature rises above 42° F. (6° C.), for this, coupled with the lengthening of the days, triggers off the growth of many plants. This point may arrive in England at any time between mid February and late March, according to the particular season; or in Scotland two or three weeks later, for April in Aberdeenshire may well be wintrier than March in the Thames valley. Just as crocuses, daffodils, and other spring bulbs start to flower earlier in our gardens in a warm, forward spring, so do wild flowers. In the remarkably early springs of 1957 and 1961, for instance, bluebells were out at the end of March, whereas in the late ones of 1956 and 1962

1. Inverewe Gardens, Wester Ross (National Trust for Scotland) it was early May before they appeared in any force; the normal date in an average year is between 15 and 25 April. Many birds, too, regulate their nesting by the general warmth; blackbirds and thrushes, for instance, start building nests and laying eggs as soon as the mean temperature in March has been above 40°F. (4°C.) for about five days.

Summer warmth is greatest in south-east England, where London has a July mean temperature of over 64°F. (18°C.), while most of England and Wales and the south-eastern part of Ireland average more than 60°F. (15°C.) at this time, and the Scottish Lowlands very nearly do so. In Scotland it gets progressively cooler as you go north, till in the Shetlands the average July temperature is 9°F. (4°C.) less than in London, although the average January temperature of London and Shetland is about the same. The northern limit of distribution of numerous animals and plants in the British Isles is determined at least partly by the fact that our summers are not warm enough.

Rainfall is the other great climatic variable that affects wildlife and especially the flora. It ranges widely in quantity, from the surprisingly dry conditions of the Thames estuary, with an average of less than twenty inches a year (there are several deserts in the world which have eighteen inches of rain a year), to the tropical wetness of parts of Snowdonia, the Lake District, and the Western Highlands of Scotland, where among the higher mountains 100 inches a year is regular. The two extremes are represented by Great Wakering near Shoeburyness in Essex, with about nineteen inches, and the summits of Snowdon and Sgurr na Cniche in Inverness-shire, with 200 inches or more. Fortunately, the greater part of inhabited Britain has a more temperate amount of rain, from twenty-five to forty inches, and the evaporation loss is probably between fourteen and eighteen inches in most of the lowland agricultural areas. Most of this takes place between April and early October; we may fairly say that wherever the annual rainfall is less than about thirty to thirty-two inches the land, in summer, tends to dry out, as the evaporation exceeds the rainfall during those months. The fact that most rain falls on the west side of Great Britain, and in Ireland, only a tiny part of which country has less than thirty inches, means that grass and vegetation generally is much lusher in the west and, thanks to the milder winters, has a longer growing period than in the east. This contributes to the great natural divide, which is also a geological one, between the highlands of the north and west and the lowlands of the south and east. It so happens that the highest ground in Britain lies on the side of the country from which most of the rain-bearing winds approach. This forces the winds to rise and drop their moisture before they reach the lower ground farther east. Ferns and other plants which like moisture, and their associated animals, are therefore commoner in the west, while plants that prefer drier conditions, such as the campion *Silene otites* and other steppe plants of the exceptionally well-drained soils of East Anglian Breckland, are found mainly, or even only, in the east. Where high rainfall does occur in the east, however, as in the hills of the Weald of Kent and Sussex, 'western' plants, such as Cornish moneywort *Sibthorpia europaea* and the filmy fern *Hymenophyllum tunbrigense* appear in sheltered habitats.

The average amount of sunshine throughout the year is by no means exactly correlated with temperature variation in the British Isles, but it is probably less important in controlling the distribution of animals and plants. Coasts are everywhere more sunny than places inland. The sunniest area lies along the south coast, from Devonshire to Suffolk, where a few places average about five hours a day. The cloudy uplands towards the north-west have considerably less; parts of the West Highlands and the hilly Shetlands average scarcely three hours daily. With these must be mentioned inner London and several of the great industrial cities, where the amount of bright sunshine is severely cut down by smoke. This situation, however, is beginning to improve. There is of course a great deal more sunshine in the summer than in the winter, the June range of eight hours a day (Isle of Wight) to five and a half hours (North Scotland, West Ireland) contrasting sharply with the December range from over one and a half hours along the south coast to under half an hour in the Shetlands.

Other meteorological phenomena, such as fog, mist, hail, and snow, influence the flora and fauna mainly insofar as they affect the temperature, rainfall, and sunshine. In the Scottish mountains there are a few north-facing slopes and corries where snow lies very late and in a bad summer almost through the year, but there is no permanent snow; Professor Gordon Manley has calculated that Ben Nevis would need to be about 900 feet higher to acquire a permanent snowfield. Though the distribution of our mountain plants is certainly affected by the length of snow cover, no distinctive snow-patch flora has developed as in high mountain ranges on the Continent. However, the harshening climate as you ascend British mountains does have a very marked effect on the vegetation. The tree line, for instance, is much lower than it is in Scandinavia; in the Peak District the oak and ash ascend only to 1,000 feet and even the birch peters out at 1,250 feet.

In a windy maritime climate the most decisive impression is made by the very rapid rate of decrease in the length of the effective growing season with altitude, as well as in the intensity of the summer warmth. Increased cloudiness, diminished evaporation, greater rainfall, and the obviously lower daytime temperatures all play their part in emphasizing the tremendous contrast between the vegetation of the sour and wet high Pennines, or the desolation of Rannoch Moor, and that of fertile Sussex or even the sheltered shores of Morecambe Bay.

GEOLOGY AND THE SOIL

Animal life depends, directly or indirectly, on plant life, and plant life is directly influenced by the soil. The soil, in turn, derives from the underlying rocks. The major soil division that affects plant life is that between lime-rich, basic, calcareous, or alkaline soil and lime-poor, hungry, or acid soil; soils which are intermediate are called neutral. Typical lime-rich soils are made by the Chalk of south-eastern England, the Oolitic Limestone of the Cotswolds, and the Carboniferous Limestone of the Craven Pennines in north-west Yorkshire. Typical acid soils are found on the Lower Greensand, which makes extensive heaths on the Surrey–Hampshire border, the Millstone Grit of the Pennines, and in the great bulk of the Scottish Highlands. Some plants, such as the rock-rose, the cowslip, and several species of orchid (Fig. 2), will thrive in Britain only on lime-rich soils; others, like the daisy, the dandelion, and the meadow buttercup, will grow on any soil, which explains why they are

2. Bee orchid. One of the orchids that grow only in lime-rich soils

so common; yet others, such as broom, ling, heather, and common cotton-grass, demand at least a slightly acid soil. This is one major factor that makes the vegetation of the British Isles so varied.

It so happens that the great geographical and physiographical divide into Highland and Lowland Britain, briefly mentioned above, also corresponds very largely to the division between predominantly calcareous and non-calcareous soils. It was sixty years ago that Sir Halford Mackinder, the great geographer, first drew attention to the fact that, if you draw a line from the mouth of the Tees to the mouth of the Exe, you divide the higher and more rugged hills and mountains of the north and west from the lower hills and plains of the south and east. At the same time you are dividing the wilder and less cultivated country, the greater rainfall, and the predominantly acid soils of the north and west from the almost entirely cultivated farmland and woodlands, the lower rainfall, and the predominantly calcareous or neutral soils of the south and east. To the naturalist this divide is just as important as it is to the farmer and the geographer.

The reason for this sharp division in soil types rests on the geological history of Britain. The calcareous rocks are more recent ones, and the rocks of Britain become older as you go north and west. The oldest rocks of all are the Lewisian gneisses of the Outer Hebrides, laid down over five hundred million years ago, and the youngest are the sands and gravels of the East Anglian 'crag' deposits that were laid down only a very few million years ago. Almost all the rocks of Scotland were laid down at least three hundred million years ago, and in Highland Britain as a whole there is very little that is not at least three hundred and fifty million years old. In all our northern and western mountain systems there are only small bands of limestone or basic rocks, and these are the very places where the rarest and most attractive alpine plants grow, as on the famous Ben Lawers in Perthshire (Fig. 3). The south and east, however, are made up of successive belts of more recent

geological formations, which stretch from south-west to north-east across England, and most of which are predominantly calcareous. The two most important are the Oolitic Limestones from Portland and Bridport in Dorset to the North York Moors, passing through the Cotswolds and Northamptonshire uplands on the way, and the Chalk, from Purbeck to Flamborough Head, which forms Salisbury Plain, the Marlborough and Berkshire Downs, the Chilterns, and the Lincolnshire and Yorkshire Wolds. In the extreme south-east the Chalk throws off two arms to the eastward, the North and South Downs.

Of course there are many variations in this broad picture. The Carboniferous Limestone of the Mendips and the Craven Pennines, the Silurian Limestone of the Wye valley, the Magnesian Limestone of County Durham, and the narrow band of limestone down the west side of Scotland, which has brought botanical fame to Inchnadamph in Sutherland, among other places, are all in the Highland zone. The hungry acid soils that give rise to the heathlands of the New Forest, southern

3. Ben Lawers, Perthshire (National Trust for Scotland)

Dorset, south-west Surrey, and the East Anglian coast are all in the lowland zone. Moreover, the picture is considerably complicated by the superficial or drift deposits that overlie the rocks in many places, especially where the glaciers of the Ice Age have been. Chalky Boulder Clay left by the glaciers gives much of East Anglia a slightly basic soil; the clay capping of the Chilterns enables acid-loving plants such as broom or heather to grow within a few yards of rock-rose and cowslip; and in south-west Norfolk and north-west Suffolk some of the most famous rarities in the British flora, the steppe plants of the Breckland, grow in acid heathland on top of Chalk rock hundreds of feet deep.

But, broadly speaking, the Highland and Lowland zones of Britain have their distinctive flora and fauna that would enable any competent naturalist, after a blindfold journey, to say at least which half of Britain he was in. Among the birds, for instance, the ring ouzel, merlin, and common sandpiper are characteristic of the northern moors, and the nightingale, red-backed shrike, and hobby of the woods and heathlands of the south. Where the ash is the tree of the downs and wolds, the mountain ash or rowan adorns the moorlands of the north and west, and there must be many northern moors and southern downs where half an hour's botanical search would turn up few species of plant common to the other, apart from the ubiquitous sheep's fescue grass. The marbled white and adonis blue butterflies of the southern downs are likewise mutually exclusive with the large heath and Scotch argus butterflies of northern moors and mosses.

As will become apparent in Chapter 4, soil differences account for most of the range of differences between the animal and plant communities of various types of habitat.

THE INFLUENCE OF MAN

Two thousand years ago the British Isles were a land of forest and marsh, thicket, swamp, and moor. All the activities of the human inhabitants during the previous two thousand years or so of primitive agriculture had scarcely affected the natural vegetation. Today, you must go to the tops of the highest mountains or a few remote coastal strands to find animal and plant communities not affected directly or indirectly by the activities of man. What we call natural is no better than semi-natural, but for that matter even tropical jungles in the heart of Africa may be semi-natural, having been once cultivated and left to revert to forest. Almost the whole of our farmland, the typical 'country' of the south, was formerly woodland, and

would revert to woodland in far less than a hundred years if a cataclysm were to destroy human but not vegetable life in Britain. To be convinced of this, all that is necessary is to visit Rothamsted Experimental Station in Hertfordshire, and see the portion of the Broadbalk Field that was left uncultivated about a hundred years ago; it is now an oakwood, indistinguishable from other oakwoods we fondly suppose to be immemorial and natural (Fig. 4). For in fact our woodland, too, is almost all artificial. The Chiltern beechwoods were mostly planted to

4. *Broadbalk Wilderness, Rothamsted, Herts.*

provide timber for the High Wycombe chair trade; the coppiced oakwoods of the Weald were planted to supply hazel for hurdles and oak for the Royal Navy, and they are disappearing because the demand for both has gone; in all Scotland the natural pinewoods are so few that they have been carefully catalogued by Professor Steven and Dr Carlisle to the number of thirty-five. Even a wood, such as Bledlow Great Wood in Buckinghamshire, which was recorded in Domesday Book, may not be an entirely natural one; it has probably been felled and replanted more than once.

It might be thought that the bleak summits of the Pennines at least were natural, but Professor Pearsall has demonstrated that the vegetation of the hills west of Manchester has in fact been wrecked by the acrid smoke of Cottonopolis. Those great sedgy hummocks, scattered among hollows of bare peat are the work of Old King Coal, not of Dame Nature. Even the bare outline of the sweeping fells is a human artefact, a thing which is often forgotten by the amenity movement when it opposes afforestation. For all our tree-planting today is re-afforestation; our hills were once all wooded up to the tree-line. The trees were felled by man, and his flocks of sheep by nibbling away at the saplings made certain that they would not grow again. If the south and east of Britain is for the most part a deliberately landscaped countryside, the work of eighteenth-century landowners who wrought better than they knew, the north and west is an accidentally landscaped countryside, the work of sheep graziers who had no idea what they were doing.

There are many other ways in which man has influenced the animal and plant populations of Britain. Game preservation, for instance, has had a deep influence, which still awaits its historian. Not only have several completely new species been introduced, notably the pheasant and the red-legged partridge, but existing stocks of other game animals, red deer, common partridge, brown trout, even mallard, have been so heavily reinforced by fresh stock bred at home or imported from the

Continent, that it is doubtful how far the present populations can be considered as native. Moreover, to protect these animals the keepers have indulged in a slaughter of predators. The polecat, the pine marten, the golden eagle, and the kite have all gone from England; the buzzard and the raven have been driven back into the west, though in recent years they have been spreading back again. By way of grim compensation, the animals they might have preyed upon, rats, rabbits, wood-pigeons, and grey squirrels, have vastly increased in the country-side and have become pests.

Indeed, most of our worst pests have been introduced accidentally or deliberately by human agency. The black and brown rats (Fig. 5) came to Britain on board ship in the Middle Ages and eighteenth century respectively; the rabbit (Fig. 6) was first imported here for its fur and meat in the twelfth century; the grey squirrel (Fig. 7) was deliberately introduced by irresponsible landowners seventy years ago; and within quite recent years muskrats, coypus, and mink have all escaped from fur farms and made a nuisance of themselves. Many insect and other invertebrate pests have also come here by human agency,

6. *Young wild rabbits*

7. *Grey squirrel*

among them the woolly aphis of apple trees, the slipper limpet which is a pest of oyster beds, and several species of cockroach.

Nor is our native flora uncontaminated by the hand of man. Besides many more or less ephemeral plants that came in with impure seed corn and now frequent cornfields and waste ground, there is a host of plants that have escaped from gardens and established themselves, such as winter heliotrope *Petasites fragrans*, the bindweed *Calystegia silvatica*, the balsam *Impatiens glandulifera*, evening primroses and red valerian. Nobody seeing the profusion of red valerian on many southern cliffs and quarries or the balsam in serried array in a Cornish combe would imagine they were anything but natives. Even some of our common trees are not native. The sycamore was introduced about five hundred years ago; the larch much more recently; the common elm, which rarely sets seed in Britain, may have been introduced as a fodder plant in the Iron Age; even the English oak may not be the rockribbed patriot it is believed to be. There are two kinds of oak in Britain, one with and the other without stalks to its acorns; the stalkless one, the durmast oak *Quercus petraea*, is found mainly in the west, and the stalked one, the pedunculate oak *Q. robur*, in the east. A great deal more pedunculate oak than durmast has been planted down the centuries, for the former is the better timber tree, and there is no certainty that the oakwoods that covered southern Britain two thousand years ago contained anything like as much pedunculate oak as is found in British woods today.

Further Reading

THE CLIMATE
Bilham, E. G., *The Climate of the British Isles*, 1938.   *General*
Manley, Gordon, *Climate and the British Scene*, 1952.

GEOLOGY AND THE SOIL
Russell, Sir E. John, *The World of the Soil*, 1957.   *England*
Stamp, L. Dudley, *Britain's Structure and Scenery*, 1946.
Regional Memoirs of the Geological Survey.

THE INFLUENCE OF MAN

Fitter, R. S. R., *London's Natural History*, 1945.

   The Ark in Our Midst: the Story of the Introduced Animals of Britain, 1959.

Ritchie, James, *The Influence of Man on Animal Life in Scotland*, 1920.

Salisbury, Sir Edward, *Weeds and Aliens*, 1961.

Stamp, L. Dudley, *Man and the Land*, 1955.

REGIONAL NATURAL HISTORY

Official Guides to National Parks and National Forest Parks.

Berlin, J., and others, *The New Forest*, 1960.

Clarke, W. G., *In Breckland Wilds*, 1925. (East Anglia.)

Dix, H. M., and Hughes, D. R., *The Coventry District: a Naturalist's Guide*. 1960.

Edwards, K. C., Swinnerton, H. H., and Hall, R. H., *The Peak District*, 1962.

Harvey, L. A., and St Leger-Gordon, D., *Dartmoor*, 1953.

Steers, J. A., *Scolt Head Island*, 1960. (Norfolk.)

Watt, Grace, *The Farne Islands*, 1951. (Northumberland.)

Wooldridge, S. W., and Goldring, Frederick, *The Weald*, 1953.

Journal: *Naturalist*. (Mainly North of England.)

Wales   Buxton, John, and Lockley, R. M., *Island of Skomer*, 1950. (Pembrokeshire.)

Lockley, R. M., *Letters from Skokholm*, 1947. (Pembrokeshire.)

North, F. J., Campbell, Bruce, and Scott, Richenda, *Snowdonia*, 1949.

Journal: *Nature in Wales.*

Scotland   Baxter, Evelyn V., and Rintoul, Leonora Jeffrey, *The Birds of Scotland*, 1953.

Darling, F. Fraser, *Natural History in the Highlands and Islands*, 1947.

Eggeling, W. J., *The Isle of May*, 1960. (Firth of Forth.)

Holden, A. E., *Plant Life in the Scottish Highlands*, 1952.

McVean, Donald N., and Ratcliffe, Derek A., *Plant Communities of the Scottish Highlands*, 1962.

Williamson, Kenneth, and Boyd, J. Morton, *St Kilda Summer*, 1960.

Steven, H.M., and Carlisle, A., *The Native Pinewoods of Scotland*, 1959.

Journals: *Scottish Birds* and *Scottish Naturalist*.

Armstrong, E.A., *Birds of the Grey Wind*, 1940. (Northern Ireland.)

Kennedy, P.G., and others, *The Birds of Ireland*, 1954.

Praeger, Robert Lloyd, *Natural History of Ireland*, 1950.
    The Botanist in Ireland, 1934.

Journal: *Irish Naturalists' Journal*.

2 Plant Life

The Plant Kingdom contains two main divisions, the higher or seed-bearing flowering plants, and the much more numerous lower plants, such as mosses and fungi, which have no flowers or seeds and are known to botanists as cryptogams.

FLOWERING PLANTS

Around 1,500 well-defined species of flowering plants are native in the British Isles, and another 600 or so are established aliens introduced by direct or indirect human agency. The alien part of our flora is thus considerably more important than the alien part of our fauna, and many plants, such as the Canadian waterweed in many lakes and rivers, monkey flower *Mimulus guttatus*, and in southern England even the Scots pine, have integrated themselves into the British flora so well that a botanist unaware of their history would probably regard them as native. How rapidly a new plant can colonize is well illustrated by the little New Zealand willow herb *Epilobium nerterioides*, which, starting from small beginnings as a garden escape fifty years ago, is now well established as a wild plant competing successfully with native vegetation in the hill districts of the north and west, especially in the Clyde Basin, the Lake District, Yorkshire, and North Wales. An even higher proportion of our weeds and plants of bare and waste ground are of recent man-aided origin, but, as the researches of Professor Godwin and others show, many of our most familiar weeds, such as dandelion, coltsfoot, and curled dock, were already present in Britain before agriculture began, and presumably grew on river banks, morainic deposits left by the retreating glaciers after the Ice Age, and other naturally bare spots.

As a result of its northerly position on the western edge of Europe, and its wide range of climatic variation, the British flora, though not as rich in species as a comparable area on the Continent, is probably more widely varied in its origin. In the south-west of both England and Ireland are a number of species, the so-called Lusitanian flora, which have their main home in south-west France and the Iberian peninsula, or even the Mediterranean. These include the strawberry tree *Arbutus unedo* of the Killarney district of County Kerry, the Cornish heath *Erica vagans* of the Lizard peninsula, and the Mediterranean heath *E. mediterranea* of western Ireland. In the east, in the dry Breckland heaths of south-west Norfolk and north-east Suffolk, are steppe plants, more at home in eastern Europe, such as the speedwell *Veronica spicata* and the rare mugwort *Artemisa campestris*. In the Highlands of Scotland grow many Arctic plants near the southern limit of their distribution, among them the oyster-plant *Mertensia maritima*, cloudberry *Rubus chamaemorus*, and the woolly willow *Salix lanata*. There is even a small North American element in the flora of western Scotland and western Ireland, possibly derived from seeds dispersed on the feet of wildfowl, for white-fronted and barnacle geese from Greenland regularly cross the Atlantic to winter in these areas. Our North American plants include the blue-eyed grass *Sisyrinchium bermudiana*, a lady's tresses orchid *Spiranthes romanzoffiana*, pipewort *Eriocaulon septangulare*, two waterweeds, a rush, and a mudwort.

There are two major divisions among our native seed-bearing plants. One is between the conifers, which bear their embryo seeds naked on the scales of cones, and the flowering plants, which conceal theirs within an ovary at the base of the flower. The flowering plants are further subdivided into the dicotyledons and the monocotyledons, according to whether their seedlings have one or two seed-leaves.

Only three species of conifer are native to Britain, and all are evergreen trees and shrubs: the Scots pine, the juniper, and the yew. Many more, however, have been planted for timber or ornamental purposes, and some of these, such as the European larch and the North American Douglas fir, readily regenerate themselves while the maritime pine *Pinus pinaster* has completely established itself over a wide area of heathland on the borders of Hampshire and Dorset.

Dicotyledons have their leaves usually broad, often stalked, and nearly always net-veined, with the parts of their flowers (sepals, petals, stamens, etc.) usually in multiples of four or five. They may be either trees or shrubs with woody stems or herbs with non-woody stems (to a botanist a herb is not just an aromatic plant used in cooking, but any non-woody plant). The most important 'dicot' families in our flora are the buttercup, cabbage, pink, peaflower, rose, carrot, figwort, labiate, and daisy families. Typical familiar wild dicotyledons are the primrose, meadow cranesbill, and red clover.

Monocotyledons, on the other hand, have their leaves usually narrow and unstalked, often parallel-sided and nearly always parallel-veined, and their flower-parts always in multiples of three. All the 'monocots' found in Britain are non-woody, with the sole exception of butcher's broom, a most curious prickly plant, whose apparent leaves are in fact flattened stems and whose real leaves are tiny scales that have to be looked for. The most important monocot families in our flora are the pondweeds, rushes, sedges, orchids, and grasses. Typical monocot wild flowers are the bluebell (in Scotland the wild hyacinth) (Fig. 8), the reed-mace or false bulrush *Typha latifolia*, and the cotton-grasses.

The grasses constitute in many ways the most important single family in the British flora, for they provide the bulk of the ground cover over most of the countryside. Many people do not realize not only that grasses are flowering plants and have flowers just as much as primroses and bluebells do, but also that our cereal crops, wheat, oats, and barley, are in fact cultivated grasses. To appreciate this, one need only compare an ear of wheat with that bane of the gardener the couch or twitch grass *Agropyron repens*, an ear of oats with the wild oat *Avena fatua*, which is a common and pestilential cornfield weed, or an ear of barley with the common roadside grass, wall barley

Hordeum murinum. Most grasslands in farming country in Britain today are artificial, and have been sown with seed mixtures after being ploughed. However, most of the grasses sown are improved strains of common British wild grasses, such as perennial ryegrass and cocksfoot.

Most people who are interested in wild plants at all find our wild orchids an irresistible attraction. There are forty-seven different species, and though quite a few are rare, many of them are common and widespread. The fact that casual walkers in the countryside so readily pick wild orchids may be one reason why others do not see them and so tend to think that all orchids are rare. The commonest orchids are the early purple, the twayblade, and the spotted orchids, of which there are two closely similar kinds, *Dactylorchis maculata* growing on acid and *D. fuchsii* on calcareous soil. The less common orchids are often common enough in their special habitats, for instance, the large white helleborine and birdsnest orchid in beechwoods, the marsh orchids *Dactylorchis incarnata* and *D. praetermissa*

8. *Wild bluebell* (*called wild hyacinth in Scotland*)

in marshes, and the fragrant and pyramidal orchids in chalk or limestone grassland. At the other extreme some of the rarer orchids are among the rarest British plants today. These include the lady's slipper with a few localities in Yorkshire whose whereabouts are a closely guarded secret; the military orchid, with one locality in Suffolk and another in the Chilterns; the monkey orchid, with two localities in Kent and one in Oxfordshire; the red helleborine with two or three localities in the Cotswolds and one in the Chilterns; and the ghost orchid *Epipogium aphyllum*, most elusive of all, which has a handful of sites in the Chilterns where it may not flower at all for years on end. Yet another class of rareness includes plants which are very local but not uncommon where they are found, such as the lady and late spider orchids in East Kent, the dense-flowered orchid *Neotinea intacta* in the west of Ireland, and the creeping lady's tresses in the eastern Highlands.

As with the grasses, it comes as a surprise to many people that trees and shrubs are flowering plants and have flowers. This is probably partly due to the misleading term 'flowering shrubs' applied to those ornamental shrubs which have conspicuous and beautiful flowers. However, shrubs with inconspicuous flowers, like the buckthorn and spindle-tree, and catkin-type flowers, like the hazel and common sallow, are just as much flowering shrubs as any others. If grasses form the carpet of the natural scenery, trees and shrubs make the furniture. They are the most conspicuous natural objects seen on any country walk. The commonest trees of hedgerows are oaks, ashes, and elms, but elms rarely form woods, so that woods are mostly pure oak, or a mixture of oak and ash; in some districts also pure woods of beech, ash, or Scots pine and mixed ones of oak and hornbeam may be found. Other trees, such as wild cherry *Prunus avium*, white beam *Sorbus aria*, and wild service tree *S. torminalis*, do not make woods, but are found scattered in woods of other species. Of course, many woods nowadays are plantations of Scots pine or alien conifers, but these species are often used as nurse crops for native trees, especially beech,

so before reproaching foresters for replanting their woods with nothing but alien conifers it is wise to take a second look and see if there are not some young beech or oak coming up in between the faster growing conifers. Hawthorn is the most commonly planted hedge plant; few other native shrubs are deliberately planted nowadays. Many other shrubs, however, contribute to the beauty of the countryside, which may be white with blackthorn blossom in April as well as with hawthorn blossom in May. The autumn tints of the chalk-loving shrubs, buckthorn, guelder rose (Fig. 9), dogwood, and wayfaring tree, all add to the pleasure of visiting the downs and wolds in late October and early November when the fiery colours of the dying beech foliage, though not vying with the maples of North America, are a fine sight in their own right.

Not a little of the pleasure of walking in the country in winter is due to the diversification of the landscape by our native evergreens, notably the ubiquitous ivy, but also holly and gorse and, in some districts, broom, yew, and juniper. Even the half-

9. Wild guelder rose

10. Old man's beard (or traveller's joy)

evergreens, such as privet and bramble, are a great help. On countless hillsides throughout the north and west acres of bracken, dark green in summer, copper-brown in winter, immensely enhance the landscape even if the farmers disapprove. In chalky districts also the dead fruiting heads of old man's beard or traveller's joy add a further contrast by festooning the bushes and hedgerows with their grey cottonwool (Fig. 10).

Ivy, traveller's joy, brambles, wild roses, honeysuckle (Fig. 11), and bittersweet or woody nightshade are our only woody climbers; in summer they are also joined by the deciduous climbers, including black and white bryonies, and several kinds of vetch. These climbers and some other straggly plants that clamber over other vegetation are also invaluable in introducing contrast into the natural landscape.

Much of the pleasure of a country walk consists in spotting and identifying individual wild flowers, but often the traveller is speeding by in car or train, and then he may have to rely on the massed effects of colonial plants for his pleasure. Many of

33

these plants appear in early spring, before the leaves are on the trees, when sunshine in the woodland lights up sheets of wood anemones, primroses, and bluebells. In spring too the gorse is in its full golden glory; it is easy to see why Linnaeus might have fallen on his knees in wonder at his first sight of it. Later in the year foxgloves may make a gay splash of colour on the woodland edge or heath, while one of the glories of the lime-stone belt that stretches from Dorset to North Yorkshire is the brilliant blue of the meadow cranesbill. On heaths and moors the purple bell-heather *Erica cinerea* makes a fine deep purple array in June and July, and is followed in August and Septem-ber by the softer purple of the well-loved heather or ling *Calluna vulgaris* that washes its colour over many moorlands from Hindhead in Surrey to the Scottish Highlands. In late summer too many coastal saltmarshes are purple with sea lavender *Limonium vulgare*.

THE FLOWERLESS PLANTS OR CRYPTOGAMS

Besides the more familiar seed-bearing flowering plants, there are a great many 'flowerless' plants or Cryptogams in Britain;

12. Boletus parasiticus *on* Scleroderma aurantium

far more species, indeed, than there are of flowering plants. The word 'cryptogam' comes from two Greek words, and means 'hidden marriage': it was bestowed upon those plants without obvious flowers or seeds by the early botanists because they had no apparent means of sexual reproduction. However, sexual reproduction is in fact as well developed in most of these plants as in the flowering plants.

Among the simplest of our cryptogamic plants are the Fungi, which lack the green pigment, chlorophyll. By means of this pigment all normal plants manufacture sugars, starch, and other organic materials from carbon dioxide gas, and water, using the energy from sunlight – the process is known as photosynthesis, and all life on earth depends on this process, directly or indirectly. Hence fungi must either live as parasites, taking their organic food from other plants (or, in some cases, animals) or as saprophytes, feeding on the dead remains of other plants.

When fungi are mentioned, many people tend to think only of toadstools and mushrooms; in fact the fungi are a vast and diverse group of plants, many of them of microscopic size (Fig. 12). They all consist fundamentally of a mycelium or

35

weft of cylindrical threads called hyphae. In the fruiting bodies of those larger fungi known as toadstools and bracket fungi, these threads are massed together to form an apparently solid structure, but if we tease out a portion of, say, a mushroom, under a lens, we can see that it is composed of a vast number of tangled white threads, the hyphae.

Fungi reproduce by means of spores. If we place the cap of a mature toadstool or mushroom gill downwards on a sheet of white paper for a while, many spores will discharge and fall on to the paper, forming a beautiful 'spore-print' of the gills. Many of the larger fungi produce spores in vast numbers; for instance, the spore production of a single giant puff-ball *Lycoperdon bovista* runs into thousands of millions.

The mushroom feeds on organic matter in the soil and is a good example of a saprophytic fungus; others are *Mucor*, the white mould that grows on old bread, and *Penicillium*, a greyish mould sometimes found on fruit or jam, from which penicillin is obtained. The yeasts (*Saccaromyces*) used in making bread, beer, wine, etc., are actually microscopic saprophytic fungi.

The rusts (*Puccinia*) are examples of parasitic fungi, of which some species grow on cereals: another stage in their life-history forms spore-containing cups called aecidia, which in the case of the wheat rust grows on the leaves of the wild barberry *Berberis vulgaris*: hence it is unwise to have barberry bushes close to a field of wheat.

The mycelia of certain toadstools make connexion with the roots of certain forest trees; other fungi are closely associated with orchid roots. In both cases the association is known as a mycorrhiza and appears to assist in the nutrition of the tree or orchid.

Thus many fungi are of great economic importance, both to other plants and to man himself, in ways both good and bad.

The Algae are another great group of fairly simple plants, but they differ from fungi in that all of them possess chlorophyll. They range from simple one-celled microscopic water plants, which can swim about by means of whip-like flagella (but are plants, not animals, because they contain chlorophyll and have a cell wall of cellulose), to huge seaweeds of many shapes and colours. All, however, have relatively simple sexual reproductive processes. *Chlamydomonas* is a good example of a unicellular green alga, found normally in fresh water, either in ponds or such places as water butts. In some simple algae groups of cells are joined together to form rounded or globular colonies: often each cell has flagella by means of which the whole colony swims about in the water. Many algae take the form of simple or branched filaments, often arranged in chains of cells, suggestive of fungal hyphae, but of course possessing chlorophyll; examples are the pond scums such as *Spirogyra*, and the branched *Draparnaldia*. Others form sheets of thin translucent tissue like the sea-lettuce *Ulva*, resembling green oiled silk in appearance.

The algae so far considered are all green and fairly small and except for the *Ulva* are largely characteristic of fresh water; but many of the larger seaweeds are red or brown owing to the presence of extra pigments besides the ever-present chlorophyll. Some of the big seaweeds have massive plant bodies of thousands or even millions of cells, but the plant is never distinguished into stem, leaves, and roots, usually consisting of a branched ribbon-like or cylindrical body called a thallus. A familiar example is the brown seaweed bladder-wrack *Fucus vesiculosus* found on rocky shores between tide-levels; the bladders which give the plant its name make it more buoyant.

Lichens, which often form grey or brown crusts on trees or rocks, or greyish bushy structures on the ground on heaths, are very peculiar plants because they represent partnerships between fungi and algae. The fungus forms the main body of the plant and the algal cells are carried inside the mass of fungal filaments. The algal cells supply organic food by photosynthesis. The fungus benefits from this food supply and in return provides the alga with a sheltered home for growth. About 2,000 species are known in Britain, but mostly in the clean air and moister climates of the north and west: they are sensitive to atmospheric pollution.

37

13. Polytrichum commune, *the largest British moss*

The Bryophyta are the next group of the flowerless plants to be considered; they consist of the Mosses and the Liverworts. Most people have often only a vague idea of the nature of mosses: they think of them as the green 'fur' one sometimes sees on trees or even on ponds, and frequently confuse them with both algae and lichens. However, mosses, with their close relatives the liverworts, form a very distinct and interesting division of the plant kingdom. All bryophytes are fairly small: the largest British moss *Polytrichum commune* (Fig. 13) is only about a foot high, and most are only a few inches long: some are minute and just visible to the naked eye. There are about 680 British mosses and 280 British liverworts.

The mosses all have a plant body containing chlorophyll, consisting of a distinct stem with leaves arranged on it, usually in a spiral manner, but they lack true roots, though tiny hairs, called rhizoids, are usually present to hold the plant to the substratum.

The liverworts are usually rather simpler and of two types of structure. Many have a stem bearing leaf-like lobes, usually in two lateral rows, sometimes with a third row of underleaves, but, unlike those of most mosses, the leaves have no veins or midribs, and may be variously lobed or divided. Moss leaves are never compound in this way. Some liverworts, however, have a rather ribbon-like forked plant body, resembling somewhat the thallus of a seaweed such as *Fucus*, without division into stem and leaves.

Although rather lowly plants, bryophytes may be quite important in the vegetation of humid places, such as the damp hill woodlands of western Britain, where they may carpet the ground and even clothe the tree-trunks to a height of several feet. The bryophytes that grow on trees are called epiphytes: they obtain their water either directly from rain, or even from water vapour in the atmosphere; their mineral salts are obtained either from the bark of the tree, or from dust washed down by the rain.

The bog mosses (*Sphagnum*) are even more important, for, by building up peat from their dead remains, they form not only potential sources of fuel but a valuable water-retaining sponge over much of our high ground, which man destroys at the cost of losing potential water supplies.

Mosses vary much in habit: some, especially those that grow on walls or rocks, form dense cushions, and some of these, such as species of *Grimmia* and *Tortula*, may have white hair-points to the leaves. Others, such as the big *Polytrichums* with their thick leaves and the common woodland *Mnium hornum*, form turf-like colonies of erect shoots. Others again have more or less prostrate stems, often branched like feathers, or miniature ferns, such as *Thuidium tamariscinum*.

Although bryophytes are dependent on water for fertilization, not all of them grow in humid places: some can tolerate periods of extreme drought, during which they curl up in a variety of characteristic ways. This behaviour may protect them in some way, but they have no protective waterproof cuticle like higher plants. Mosses that have been dried in a herbarium for twenty years have grown when they were moistened.

The remaining groups of flowerless plants are the vascular cryptogams, the Ferns, Club-mosses, and Horsetails. These have a proper conducting system for water and dissolved food, and are organized like the seed-bearing plants, into stems, roots, and leaves, with a waterproof cuticle controlling water loss, pierced with breathing pores or stomata: such plants are true denizens of the land. But, like the more lowly bryophytes, they have an Achilles' heel: they still need external water for sexual fertilization.

The most important group of vascular cryptogams in Britain is the ferns. Though conspicuous in our woodlands and on our hillsides, particularly in the west, the ferns, with only forty-eight species, are poorly represented in the British flora, compared with the tropics. Most of our ferns are notable for their relatively large, usually highly dissected leaves or fronds, which arise either from a short stout erect stem, as in the common male fern or from a long, creeping, often underground rhizone, as in the bracken. A few, such as hartstongue fern (Fig. 14) and the peculiar adder's tongue fern, have undivided leaves. The spores are borne in small capsules called sporangia in clusters known as sori, normally on the underside of the fronds; the sori are usually protected by little flaps known as indusia. The various arrangements of the sporangia and sori are one of the bases of the classification of the ferns, so that spore-bearing parts are often needed for identification.

Some of our ferns show great differences from the normal pattern: in the adder's tongue and moonwort the frond is forked into two branches one of which bears an undivided leaf-like blade (adder's tongue) or leaflets arranged pinnately (moonwort), while the other bears the sporangia, either fused together into a simple spike (adder's tongue) or on a branch

*14. Harts-
tongue fern*

which is pinnately divided (moonwort). The filmy ferns (*Hymenophyllum* and *Trichomanes*) have as the name implies a delicate texture: the fronds are small and have leaflets which are translucent and only one cell thick, except for the veins, and the sori are purse-shaped in *Hymenophyllum* and tubular in *Trichomanes*. These filmy ferns are plants of moist humid climates, often on damp shady rocks, and are largely confined to the west of Britain and Ireland.

The club-mosses (*Lycopodium*) and the horsetails (*Equisetum*) have similar life-cycles to the ferns, and thus are often called the fern allies: but they are not really closely related. They are the modern survivors of very ancient groups of plants, which were already distinct from the ferns in the Carboniferous period when the moist forests which formed our coal measures grew. In those times the ancestors of the club-mosses and horsetails formed large trees which reached heights of up to a hundred feet; but, like the giant reptiles of the later Jurassic period, these great plants have all disappeared, either through climatic changes or from competition from the seed-bearing plants, or from both causes. We are left today with a few relatively small club-mosses and horsetails.

The British club-mosses comprise today five species of *Lycopodium*, and one of *Selaginella*; they are small creeping or erect plants found on moors or heaths. They have small, narrow, pointed leaves, superficially moss-like, and carry their spores in cones borne on the end of erect stems. *Selaginella selaginoides* is like a small marsh club-moss: it grows normally in moist calcareous places on mountains or northern sand dunes.

The quillworts (*Isoetes*) are queer plants related to *Selaginella*: they have long narrow quill-like leaves, and two of our three species grow under water, *I. lacustris* being characteristic of the stony beds of mountain lakes and tarns.

Finally, the horsetails (*Equisetum*), of which we have nine species and two hybrids, are readily distinguished by their hollow jointed stems and collar-like rings of tiny sheathing leaves. Some are unbranched, the others have branches in whorls at the joints (nodes) like the ribs of an umbrella. They bear cones at the apex of the stems.

Some species (e.g. *Equisetum arvense*, the common horsetail of waysides and waste ground) bear their cones on brown un-branched stems in spring, then produce green vegetative stems with whorls of branches and no cones in the summer. Others produce their cones on the green shoots in summer. The Dutch rush *E. hyemale* is always devoid of whorled branches; most species have simple branches, but *E. sylvaticum*, for example, bears branches which are themselves branched.

The marestail (*Hippuris*) is often confused with the horse-tails because of its whorled leaves; but it is a flowering plant, and the tiny flowers can be easily seen in the leaf axils.

Flowerless plants are less well known than the flowering

plants, but they are of immense variety and interest. It is worth noting that, except for the fungi, they are much easier to collect and preserve than the flowering plants.

Further Reading

FLOWERING PLANTS

Butcher, R.W., *A New Illustrated British Flora*, 2 vols., 1961.

Clapham, A.R., Tutin, T.G., and Warburg, E.F., *Flora of the British Isles*, 1962. Volumes of illustrations by Sybil J. Roles are in course of publication.

Dandy, J.E., *List of British Vascular Plants*, 1958.

Forsyth, A.A., *British Poisonous Plants*, 1954.

Gathorne-Hardy, Robert, *Wild Flowers in Britain*, 1938.

Gilmour, John, and Walters, Max, *Wild Flowers*, 1954.

Godwin, H., *The History of the British Flora*, 1956.

Gurney, Robert, *Trees of Britain*, 1958.

Hubbard, C.E., *Grasses*, 1954.

Hutchinson, John, *British Wild Flowers*, 2 vols., 1955.

Hyde, H.A., *Welsh Timber Trees*, 3rd ed., 1962.

McClintock, David, and Fitter, R.S.R., *The Pocket Guide to Wild Flowers*, 1956.

McClintock, David, *Supplement to the Pocket Guide to Wild Flowers*, 1957.

Matthews, J.R., *Origin and Distribution of the British Flora*, 1955.

Ross-Craig, S., *Drawings of British Plants*, 1948–.

Summerhayes, V.S., *Wild Orchids of Britain*, 1951.

Turrill, W.B., *British Plant Life*, 1948.

FUNGI

Brooks, F.T., *Plant Diseases*, 1928.

Gwynne-Vaughan, H.C.I., and Barnes, B.F., *The Structure and Development of the Fungi*, 1937.

Ramsbottom, J., *Mushrooms and Toadstools*, 1953.

ALGAE

Chapman, V.J., *The Algae*, 1962

Fritsch, F.E., *The Structure and Reproduction of the Algae*, 2 vols., 1935, 1945.

LICHENS

Duncan, U.K., *A Guide to the Study of Lichens*, 1959.

BRYOPHYTA

Jewell, A., *The Observer's Book of Mosses and Liverworts*, 1955.
Watson, E.V., *Mosses and Liverworts*, 1955.
Dixon, H.N., *Student's Handbook of British Mosses*, 1924.
MacVicar, S.M., *Student's Handbook of British Hepatics*, 1960.

FERNS, CLUB-MOSSES, AND HORSETAILS

Ferguson, Daniel, *British Ferns, Club-mosses and Horsetails*, 1924.
Clapham, Tutin, and Warburg, *Flora of the British Isles*, 1962.
Hyde, H.A., and Wade, A.E., *Welsh Ferns*, 1948.

3 Animal Life

The Animal Kingdom can broadly be divided into animals with backbones, the vertebrates, including mammals, birds, reptiles, amphibians, and fishes, and the great array of animals without backbones, the invertebrates, ranging from slugs, snails, and lobsters to butterflies, beetles, spiders, and many minute creatures visible only under a microscope.

MAMMALS

The British Isles are not rich in mammals, having only forty-one native terrestrial species, to which must be added eleven established aliens. There are also some two dozen marine mammals, two of them seals, the remainder whales, most of which are merely visitors to the British seas. Not counting the Primates, of which man is the sole representative, eight natural orders of mammals are represented in the British fauna: insectivores, bats, carnivores, seals, ungulates, lagomorphs, rodents, and whales. Few mammals are likely to be seen in the course of an ordinary country walk: mammal watchers have to go and look for their quarry much more determinedly than bird watchers.

Our seven insectivores include the widespread and familiar mole and hedgehog (Fig. 15), though the mole is better known by the sight of its molehills than in the flesh, and five species of shrew, three widespread (common, pigmy, and water shrews) and two confined respectively to the islands of Islay and Scilly. The Scilly shrew, belonging to a genus (*Crocidura*) hitherto unrecognized in the British Isles, has the distinction of being the most recently discovered native British mammal; it was named as new to science in 1924.

Twelve species of bat breed as natives in the British Isles, and one, the mouse-eared bat *Myotis myotis*, has recently been

15. Hedgehog

*16. Greater
horseshoe bat*

17. Fox cubs at ease and alert

found to be an occasional visitor to the south of England from across the Channel. The commonest and most widespread British bats are the pipistrelle (the smallest), the noctule (the largest), the long-eared bat, the greater and lesser horseshoe bats (Fig. 16), and three close relatives of the mouse-eared bat, the whiskered, Natterer's, and Daubenton's bats. Most people know bats only from seeing them fly in the dusk (though daytime flying, especially by noctules in early spring, is quite regular), or perhaps from encountering them as accidental visitors in the house. To see them at close quarters, one must seek them in their daytime roosts in hollow trees, caves, and old buildings.

To our eight native carnivores, the fox (Fig. 17), otter, badger, stoat, weasel, polecat, pine marten, and wild cat will soon be added the mink, if vigorous steps are not taken to eradicate this fur-farm escape, which will create havoc among our wildfowl if it establishes itself. Foxes, stoats, and weasels are the most often seen; badgers and otters, though widespread,

47

18. *Avocet*

usually need to be watched for. Both our native seals, the grey and the common, are widespread around our coasts, the grey mainly on rocky ones.

Only two species of ungulates, or hoofed animals, are certainly native in Britain, the red deer, found mainly in the Scottish Highlands, and the roe deer, which is much more widespread. Nowadays our woods also contain four introduced species of deer, the long-established fallow, together with the Japanese or sika deer, the muntjac or barking deer, and the Chinese water deer, all three Asiatic species which have escaped from parks. There are also wild goats, descended from medieval domestic stock, in many hill districts in the north and west.

Lagomorphs mean the rabbits and hares, of which we possess two natives, the brown and blue hares, and one alien, the rabbit, which, with the grey squirrel, is still the wild mammal most likely to be seen on a country walk. Our eleven rodents include the red squirrel, the dormouse, three species of mice, and five kinds of vole, two of them confined to Raasay and the Orkneys. To these must be added five alien pests, the grey squirrel, coypu, house mouse, and black and brown rats, and one alien not yet proved to be a pest, the fat dormouse, which is confined to the Chilterns.

Some two dozen different kinds of whale have been reported from British seas, including the killer whale, sperm whale, and narwhal, but those most likely to be seen offshore are the common porpoise and bottle-nosed dolphin.

BIRDS

Rather more than 200 different species of bird breed regularly in the British Isles, a quarter of them being summer visitors only. It is impossible to be more precise because the breeding status of some birds, such as the Kentish plover and spotted crake, is obscure. Moreover the list is constantly altering; within the past forty years the black redstart, little ringed plover, and collared dove, hitherto unknown, have established themselves as regular breeding species, while the avocet (Fig. 18), black-tailed godwit, and osprey, which had become extinct, have returned. Comparatively few of our breeding birds are established aliens; among them are the pheasant, red-legged partridge, Canada goose, mandarin duck, and little owl (Fig. 19). The capercaillie is a former native that has become

19. Little owl

re-established from introduced stock, and perhaps this is also
the status of the mute swan. Only one species of bird that has
bred in Britain in historic times has become completely extinct,
the great auk.

*20. Cock
chaffinch*

In addition there are some ninety to a hundred more or less
regular winter visitors or passage migrants. Both come to us
from northern Europe and the Arctic, including Greenland,
but the passage migrants are seen only in spring and autumn
while travelling to and from their northern breeding grounds,
passing on to warmer and more southern lands around the
Mediterranean and in Africa to spend the winter, along with
most of our summer visitors. In recent years, with intensive
watching at coastal bird observatories, several birds, such as
the icterine warbler and ortolan bunting, have been found to
be much more regular passage migrants than was previously
thought. Finally, there are more than 250 occasional or irregular
bird visitors; the exact number again is hard to determine.
However, hardly a year goes by without a new bird being added

to the British list. In 1961 the new birds were a river warbler *Locustella fluviatilis* from eastern Europe on Fair Isle, between the Orkneys and Shetlands, and a North American fox sparrow *Passerella iliaca* in Northern Ireland.

Eighteen different major groups of birds are represented among our breeding birds and regular visitors, the largest being the song birds and the group which includes the gulls, terns, and waders. On an ordinary country walk, however, it is the song birds which predominate. During spring and early summer, the songs of the blackbird, song and mistle thrushes, robin, hedgesparrow, wren, skylark, chaffinch (Fig. 20), and yellowhammer can hardly fail to be heard, and in wooded or bushy country in the south from April to June they will be joined by the nightingale, which sings by day as often as by night, and by several kinds of warbler: blackcap, whitethroat, chiffchaff, and willow and garden warblers. Song continues throughout the day, though more intensively in the morning and evening, and no bird watcher should miss the experience of hearing the massed bird choirs at the dawn chorus, which is at its best in May, when the sun rises around 5 a.m. B.S.T. To get the full effect, it is best to be in the field an hour before sunrise.

If the song birds contribute most to our enjoyment by ear, many bird watchers would vote for the birds of prey as affording the greatest pleasure to bird watching by eye. The sight of a peregrine stooping on its prey, for instance, is one of the supreme sights of the natural world, an efficiently adapted machine working at its highest pitch of accuracy. The commonest diurnal bird of prey of the countryside generally is the kestrel, easily told by its habit of hovering to search for its prey. Unfortunately it has much decreased on the eastern side of Britain in recent years, largely, it is thought, owing to having eaten mice and other prey that had been poisoned by eating seed-corn dressed with certain highly toxic insecticides. A few years ago the sparrowhawk could have been set down as our second commonest diurnal bird of prey, but this has decreased even more disastrously, especially in eastern England where, in Lincolnshire for instance, it is now virtually extinct as a breeding bird. This decline has been attributed partly to game preserving, for the sparrowhawk is our only unprotected bird of prey. The buzzard is now again quite common in western Britain, especially in Devon and Cornwall, and other birds of prey that the holidaymaker may not unhopefully expect to see are the golden eagle in the remoter Highlands, the peregrine around our cliffed coasts, and the merlin on many moors in northern and western Britain. Some birds of prey, however, are among our rarest breeding birds: the osprey has one well-known and well-guarded pair in Inverness-shire, but the marsh harrier has of recent years sunk to a very few pairs (it has become extinct in Norfolk after a generation of revival) and the kite continues to hang on with a dozen or so pairs in mid-Wales.

One of the most spectacular phenomena of the bird world is the half-yearly migration of millions of birds to and from our shores: our summer visitors from Africa and the Mediterranean arriving between March and May to displace the winter visitors departing to northern Europe and the Arctic, and the whole process being reversed again from August to November. It used to be thought that migration could be seen only on the coast, but in fact the southward autumn migration of the skylark, for instance, can be seen almost anywhere in England by just looking upwards between the hours of eight and ten on mornings in late September and October. The larger gulls too can often be seen flying overhead in spring and autumn migration, while redwings and curlews, to name only two, can be heard flying over at night even in the middle of London. Observations by radar have recently given us some inkling of the enormous volume of migration that goes on across the North Sea in almost every month of the year, either at night or too high to be seen by the naked eye by day. Only when strong adverse winds force the birds down near the ground do we realize what is happening. In this way thousands of birds

21. Edible frog

such as rooks, starlings, lapwings, and thrushes reach our shores every autumn and return north-eastwards the following spring.

REPTILES AND AMPHIBIANS

Six species each of reptiles and amphibians are native to the British Isles. The reptiles are three lizards, including the snake-like slow-worm, and three snakes. The amphibians are three newts, two toads, and a frog; in addition two introduced species of frog, the edible and marsh frogs (Fig. 21), have established themselves in some ponds in the south of England. St Patrick has gained undeserved credit for banishing from Ireland the snakes which never reached there, and in fact of this dozen species only the smooth newt and the common lizard are certainly Irish natives; the common frog was introduced there by a Fellow of Trinity College, Dublin, in 1699. Several species are confined to England: the grass snake is widespread there, but the smooth snake, sand lizard, and natterjack toad are much

53

more local. The reptiles and amphibians most likely to be encountered on an ordinary country walk are thus the grass snake, adder or viper, slow-worm, common lizard (Fig. 22), common frog, and common toad; masses of frogspawn in ponds are a familiar country sight in early spring. The adder is our only poisonous reptile; toads, and also frogs, secrete a poisonous substance which can be used to force a larger animal which has seized them to desist, but unlike snakes they have no venom.

FISHES

Fishes can conveniently be divided into freshwater and marine, although in fact there are about eighteen British species which can or do spend part of their lives in both fresh and salt water, most notably of course the salmon, sea trout, and eel. All the eels in British fresh waters are born in the Atlantic Ocean near the Sargasso Sea and make their way here by themselves; there is currently a controversy as to whether any of them ever return. A few other species, such as the flounder, which used to ascend the Severn as far as Shrewsbury, may come up our rivers from the estuaries or the sea. Apart from these, however, we have some twenty-seven fish that spend all their lives in fresh water, and about fifty which regularly live in the inshore waters of the sea. A much larger number, of course, frequent our offshore waters: the total number of fishes on the official list published by the Natural History Museum is no fewer than 367 but a great many of these are rare stragglers from Mediterranean, subtropical, or Arctic waters.

Fish are usually the concern of the angler and the aquarist rather than the naturalist, who on his country walks is pleased if he can as much as spot a brown trout in a pool under a foot-bridge or hazard a guess that smaller fishes must be minnows. Nor are marine fish any more often seen, except by those who deliberately search the rock pools for blennies, gobies, and the father lasher, the marine equivalent of the miller's thumbs of our streams. There is one large fish, however, that may be

*22. Common
lizard with
young*

conspicuous, and that is the basking shark, one of the largest
fishes in the world, which can attain a length of thirty-five or
forty feet, and whose tall dorsal fin sometimes projects from
the sea of our western coasts; it is quite inoffensive and need
cause no alarm to bathers.

INVERTEBRATES

Amongst the invertebrates a fascinating world of small animals
awaits discovery by the interested and intelligent naturalist.
These creatures – snails, woodlice, millipedes, centipedes,
harvestmen, mites, spiders, plant-bugs, and grasshoppers, to
mention a few, have been rather sadly neglected by naturalists.
Some of them have unfortunately been held in contempt by
gardeners. Certain slugs and snails can make a nuisance of
themselves, but only about half a dozen of the British land
molluscs are pests, and they have unfortunately given a bad
name to the group as a whole.

Almost any country hedgerow, especially on a grassy bank,

is a good place to begin a search. A few screw-top jars or smaller glass collecting tubes is all you need – and a sharp pair of eyes. The real enthusiast will go out at night to search by torchlight – and he will not be disappointed. The 'night shift' is often difficult to find by day because its members are so well hidden away in the earth, deeply buried in litter and under stones and in other places.

Slugs and snails are so well known as to warrant no detailed description of their characters. Slugs are really snails which have lost, or almost lost, all traces of a shell. Snails need calcium carbonate to make their shells; they also need a good deal of water to make the slime on which they glide over the surfaces of

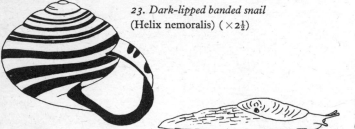

23. *Dark-lipped banded snail*
(Helix nemoralis) ($\times 2\frac{1}{2}$)

24. *Grey field slug* (Agriolimax reticulatus) ($\times 2\frac{1}{2}$)

the earth, stones, tree-trunks, and herbaceous plants. Water is even more essential for slugs, for they have no shells to stop excessive evaporation from their bodies. That is why they usually come out at night when the air is moister and there is less risk of drying up. Land molluscs are therefore usually more numerous in damp places and above all in limestone districts, where the rocks and soil contain a high proportion of calcium carbonate.

Two common species of snail can be found in almost any hedge-bank. They look very much alike, and when fully grown are about an inch across and somewhat less in height. Their usual colour is a yellowish or yellowish-brown background with up to five dark stripes running up the shell in a spiral. These stripes may be absent, or all five may be joined into one broad band. One of these two, the dark-lipped banded snail

Helix nemoralis (Fig. 23), has a dark rim to the opening of the shell and the other, the white-lipped banded snail *H. hortensis*, as its name implies, has a pale lip. In general some specimens of these snails look dark and others look much lighter. This appears to favour the survival of the species. In the earlier part of the year, before foliage has developed, thrushes pick out the darker individuals more easily. Later, when the leaves have grown, the lighter ones are more conspicuous in the darker habitat, and so the numbers of light and dark individuals eaten by thrushes in a season is about equal.

There are about two dozen kinds of slugs in Great Britain. The grey field slug *Agriolimax reticulatus* (Fig. 24), which occurs almost everywhere, including gardens, is probably the best-known species; it is about 3·5 cm. long when fully grown. The large black or dark grey *Arion ater* is also common and could scarcely be missed in a hedge-bank, or climbing up a tree trunk after dark. *Limax maximus*, another large slug, is distinctly spotted. This species has a remarkable mating habit. Two slugs suspend themselves from a twig or branch, each on a thick thread of mucus; in this position the individuals come together in mid-air and sperm exchange takes place. With two exceptions the British land molluscs are hermaphrodite, that is, each individual has both male and female organs.

The Millipedes and Centipedes are two groups of animals whose members are almost sure to be encountered in a search for slugs and snails. Both live in leaf litter among the base of grass and other herbaceous plants as well as under logs and amongst débris at the bottom of hedgerows. Millipedes are herbivorous, but centipedes are carnivorous. It is therefore important to be able to distinguish them. Centipedes are the gardener's friend, while some, but by no means all, millipedes are liable to turn from their normal diet of wild plants to onions, potatoes, and other crops. Despite their popular names it is no use counting the legs. Look at one of the rings or segments in the middle of the body. If it has two pairs of legs it is a millipede; if only one then it is a centipede. Most millipedes are rather round-backed and they have the curious habit of coiling into a sort of 'watch-spring' when disturbed. Centipedes are flattened and when picked up are only too ready to show their agility to speed on, a characteristic of so many creatures which chase and eat other animals. There are just over forty species of millipedes in Great Britain, and about the same number of centipedes.

One commoner millipede is the spotted snake millipede *Blaniulus guttulatus* (Fig. 25). It is a typical example of the group, between fourteen and eighteen millimetres long when adult, and of a greyish colour with a row of reddish spots along each side of the body. It occurs in many situations including gardens and fields, both in the soil and in decaying plant

25. *A typical millipede* (×2½)

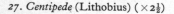

27. *Centipede* (Lithobius) (×2½)

26. *Pill millipede* (Glomeris marginata) (×5)

material on the ground. On this it probably feeds, as well as on living plant tissues including, when it gets the chance, garden vegetables, though it can probably gain entry to potatoes, onions, and carrots only after some other injury to the plant. The pill millipede *Glomeris marginata* (Fig. 26) is another quite common species often found in hedgerows and amongst scrub litter on the ground, especially if the soil is at all chalky. This species rolls itself into a ball when disturbed and is usually very reluctant to uncurl. It is then about the size of a small pea and is usually black, though reddish-yellow varieties are not uncommon.

There are a number of common and widely distributed centipedes, and members of the genus *Lithobius* (Fig. 27) are perhaps most often encountered. These fast-moving animals have fifteen pairs of legs and their body is brownish and flat. Some members of this genus attain a length of more than an inch. A somewhat less active group of centipedes with thirty-seven or more pairs of legs is also well represented in our fauna. This is the *Geophilomorpha* (Fig. 28), which are mostly rather thin delicate pale yellow or reddish creatures, and which are easily damaged if care is not taken when capturing them. Some species leave a phosphorescent trail behind them which may be seen on damp walls or near drains or other moist situations after nightfall. Centipedes feed on other small invertebrates such as insects or their larvae, spiders, harvest-spiders, young woodlice, and young worms. Like some millipedes, some centipedes burrow into the earth.

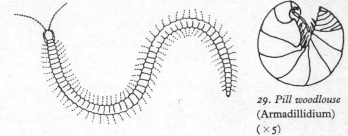

28. A geo-philomorph centipede (×4)

29. Pill woodlouse (Armadillidium) (×5)

Millipedes, centipedes, and woodlice have one important feature in common. None of them has a waxy waterproof cuticle or outer part of the skin, such as occurs in insects. Thus they are obliged to live in moist surroundings, and, like molluscs, are usually active in the evening and during the night. This restricts their distribution and the kind of places in which they can live.

The name woodlouse has probably arisen from a very common species, *Oniscus asellus*, which is not only one of the largest of the British woodlice, but frequently occurs behind the bark of old trees, in old logs and stumps, as well as under stones and in hedgerow litter. Woodlice may be found in large numbers together. Of the thirty-eight British species many occur in the sort of places where millipedes and centipedes are found, though they do not normally inhabit the soil. The pill woodlouse *Armadillidium vulgare* (Fig. 29), a common and curious species, is often met with in habitats similar to those of the pill milli-pede, with which it is easily confused. It rolls up into a grey or blackish-grey ball of about the same size. Careful examina-tion of a rolled-up pill woodlouse reveals a number of small segments on one part of the body, which are lacking in the pill millipede. If the animal can be induced to uncurl, which it is normally quite willing to do, seven pairs of legs will be seen, at once distinguishing it from the pill millipede, which has seven-teen pairs of legs. The pill woodlouse can occasionally be seen wandering about in hot sunshine. Experiments have shown that different species of woodlice differ in the length of time which they can survive away from dampness. When the pill wood-louse is found wandering in broad daylight, this appears to be a survival reaction as the habitat becomes drier; the animal is then obliged to come out of hiding and seek a moister situation in order to survive.

Woodlice appear to feed on almost anything, though most species show a preference for dead or decaying plant material, and to this extent the group as a whole probably performs a useful scavenging service in the economy of the earth's surface. There are a few species of economic importance, with records of seedlings or plants with very soft tissues being attacked, especially in greenhouses; and woodlice may attack mush-rooms. Others willingly devour material of animal origin.

The spiders are perhaps the best-known group of inverte-brates in the sense that they are frequently seen. Any country walk, stroll in a park, or afternoon session in the garden will produce a number of these interesting arachnids. The related harvest-spiders also belong to the Arachnida, which group is distinguished from insects by having four, instead of two, pairs of walking legs, a body in two instead of three parts, a complete absence of wings, and no true life-cycle. Folklore and super-stition have surrounded spiders, and it is a popular misconcep-tion that the females always eat the males, and that they all make webs, to say nothing of the prejudice against the large hairy and long-legged house spiders (*Tegenaria*) which are occasionally found in rooms or in the bath or kitchen sink, and which are promptly dispatched to eternity with the aid of the nearest long-handled brush.

Agelena labyrinthica is a fairly large spider and in general appearance not unlike the house spiders. It has a series of light-coloured bars on each side of the abdomen. The rambler's attention is usually drawn to this spider by the conspicuous and rather irregular sheet-web draped over the long grass. The web leads, usually more or less centrally, into a very distinct funnel at the bottom of which the spider sits ready to rush out and seize anything which happens to fall or alight on the web. A small piece of vegetation discreetly poked into the mesh usually induces the owner to appear. *Agelena*'s web is especially conspicuous when it is covered with September dew.

Only certain families of spiders build the typical orb webs which one sees strung from branches in the hedgerow or amongst tall foliage. The family Argiopidae is represented by a number of species, including the fat and conspicuous cross spider *Araneus diadematus* which is sure to be encountered. It is rather a round brownish spider with a conspicuous white cross on the back which, in former times, earned for it a mystical reputation. The purpose of an orb web is obvious enough, but how it came in the course of evolution is another matter. It has been suggested that since spiders are one of the major enemies of insects, that both groups were formerly ground and plant dwellers, and that insects evolved wings to evade their arachnid enemies. Later spiders evolved the web to catch the insects which had developed the habit of flying! The making of an orb web is well worth watching, for with one exception (a caddis-fly larva) it is the only trap deliberately made by an animal. The fascinating story of the spider's web is told by T. H. Savory in his book of that title.

The hunting or wolf spiders of the family Lycosidae are, for the most part, medium-sized, brownish rather nondescript arachnids. They do not spin webs but hunt small insects, wood-lice, and other invertebrates by simply running them down by sheer speed. Wolf-spiders are often very abundant on banks, the woodland floor, and on the ground generally.

Of about 600 species of British spiders, about half belong to the family Linyphiidae or money-spiders. They are all small, active web-spinners and seem to reach their maximum numbers towards the end of the summer.

At about the same time as money-spiders abound in the fields, banks, and hedgerows, some very long-legged spider-like creatures are sure to be noticed, for at this season most of

30. Harvest-spider (Phalangium opilio) ($\times 1\frac{2}{3}$)

our twenty-one British species of harvest-spiders become adult. Harvest-spiders, or Opiliones, are not very closely related to true spiders; they have no silk glands and so cannot make webs of any sort. They can be distinguished from them by the body which appears to be in one piece. It is not sharply marked off into two divisions as in spiders. The second pair of legs is by far the longest and there are only two eyes set on a little bump near the front end of the body. True spiders have four, six, or eight eyes.

The long-legged harvest-spiders most likely to be seen are the two species of *Leiobunum* or *Phalangium opilio* (L.) (Fig. 30). The length of their limbs is a great aid to clambering quickly

31. *Two common dragonflies*

(a) Libellula quadrimaculata,

(b) Aeshna juncea

amongst tall grass and other plants, which they do more readily on a dull, moist day, or in the cool of the evening. Search on the ground among the herbs is likely to reveal a smaller, much shorter-legged harvest-spider. This is *Nemastoma lugubre* and is quite unmistakable, black with two white spots. Its short legs are better fitted to moving among the closely growing stems of the plants near the ground and in moss.

In Great Britain there are just over 20,000 known species of Insects. Some, like certain butterflies, dragonflies (Fig. 31a and b), bees, and flies, are among the most familiar creatures of the countryside. Differing from the arachnids in having the body in three parts, three pairs of legs, a pair of antennae, and a definite life-cycle (egg, larva, sometimes chrysalis or pupa, and the adult) the insects present the widest range of differences in structure, colour, physiology, habits, and ecology of any group of animals. It is impossible to do justice to them here, and the reader is referred to the excellent book by Imms which deals with the natural history of this group in a most readable and interesting way.

One of the first insects likely to be met by the rambler in the early part of the year is the brimstone butterfly. This beautiful yellow creature (the female is greenish-yellow) is often awakened from hibernation by the first warm sun, sometimes even in January. It is the only British butterfly which hibernates in the open, choosing a thick evergreen bush to shelter it from the rigours of the winter. There are other striking and well-known butterflies (Fig. 32) and moths, some of which, like the red admiral, small tortoiseshell, and the cabbage whites, are familiar to most countrygoers. But the majority of this order of insects, the Lepidoptera, are not often noticed by the casual observer,

32. Comma butterfly

and some like the clothes moths and their relations are small and are only noticed when they make a nuisance of themselves by attacking crops or stored produce; and then, as often as not, it is too late to stop their depredations. But among the 2,200 Lepidoptera of Britain there is a marvellous wealth of interest and ingenious ways of protection. Some moths mimic pieces of bark, the larvae of others look like twigs; a number adopt the gaudiest colours to warn would-be attackers that they are unfit to eat. Others, small dark brownish-black and white moths, just sit about anywhere on leaves and branches and are mistaken for bird droppings!

Our beetles or Coleoptera number about 3,700. They, too, show almost unbelievable diversity of form, colour, physiology, and life history. The ladybirds (Coccinellidae) are a well-known group and frequently inhabit bushes, hedge-banks, and many kinds of plant. The two-spotted ladybird (*Adalia bipunctata*) (Fig. 33), like most of its relatives, can often be seen eating aphids or greenflies, which belong to the insect order of the Hemiptera, and not infrequently, on the same plant, one can see ants (Hymenoptera) 'milking' the aphids for their sweet secretion called honeydew. There must therefore be some biological competition between the ants and ladybirds. The aphids suffer not only from these but also from the attacks of small hymenopterous parasites which lay their eggs on them and whose larvae eventually kill them by eating through their internal organs. Birds also eat aphids, which make up for all these losses by an astonishing fecundity and rate of reproduction. This example is only one – and a comparatively simple one – of the dramatic 'web of life' enacted every day in hedgerow, meadow, wood, and garden.

33. Two-spotted ladybird (Adalia bipunctata) (×2½)

The Hymenoptera, including the ants, bees, wasps, sawflies (Fig. 34), and ichneumon-flies, number over 6,100 species in Britain. They are seconded by the true flies or Diptera with some 5,200 species. Many of the Hymenoptera have an effective method of offence or defence. The wasps often seen on the flowers of cow parsley and wild parsnip are well-known

65

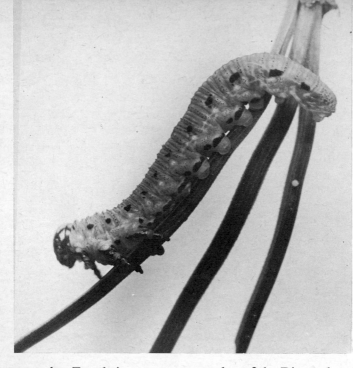

examples. For obvious reasons a number of the Diptera have found it pays to mimic them, though they themselves are quite harmless, and some bear a strong resemblance to certain members of the Hymenoptera. It is not difficult to distinguish a hymenopteron from a dipteron; the former has two pairs of wings, the latter only one pair. The collector is advised to handle Hymenoptera and Diptera with forceps when removing them from the net until ability to identify them with certainty has been mastered!

Everyone is familiar with bumble bees (*Bombus*). But how many naturalists could recognize even a few of our nineteen species, or any of the six closely related species of *Psithyrus* or cuckoo-bees? Bumble bees are among the most fascinating of insects and are good subjects for simple experiments by naturalists. They nearly always visit flowers which have irregularly arranged petals, such as members of the pea, dead-nettle, and mint families. What species of flowers are visited? What happens when the petals of all the flowers on a plant are removed? Are the flowers then visited by bumble bees? These, and other simple observations, especially on colour perception, could provide an entertaining and instructive summer after-noon's observation, especially for the less energetic of country lovers. A whole book by Free and Butler has been devoted to bumble bees and should be consulted by those interested in these insects.

Mention of the word 'fly' not unnaturally brings to mind such unpleasantries as house-flies, blue-bottles, and perhaps

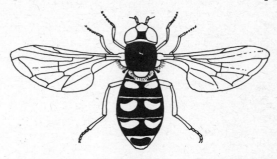

35. Hover-fly
(Syrphus
oniger) (×3½)

mosquitoes or midges. Many are of considerable economic importance; their larvae may attack crops, or parasitize animals, or transmit disease. On the pleasanter and more profitable side we may consider the hover-flies (*Syrphidae*) (Fig. 35), which are not only found in lanes, woods, and in almost any part of the country, but which do good service to man through their larvae which feed on aphids. A hot summer's afternoon is favoured by most hover-flies. They seem to stand still in the air. But the slightest movement made too close to a hover-fly causes its immediate departure with a speed which defies the observer even to guess in which direction it has gone. Many hover-flies resemble various species of wasp or bee, and the two kinds of insects can often be seen sitting together on umbellifers and other hedgerow flowers.

It is not possible in this short review to mention all the groups of invertebrates, and the insects in particular must receive scant treatment. The reader is therefore recommended to con-sult the reading list at the end of the chapter. No longer can it be said that there is no suitable literature for identification of most of the invertebrate groups, neither is it so inaccessible or technical as to be beyond the scope of the modern naturalist. True, there are deficiencies, and especially so in our knowledge of the biology of many of the lesser known and relatively un-studied groups. Here is an exciting new field of study and observation, and a challenge to the enterprising naturalist who is prepared to forgo a collection of pretty looking objects for the honour and satisfaction of discovery.

Further Reading

MAMMALS

Blackmore, Michael, *Mammals in Britain*, 1948.   *General*

Burton, Maurice, *Wild Animals of the British Isles*, 1960.

Leutscher, Alfred, *Tracks and Signs of British Animals*, 1960.

Matthews, L. Harrison, *British Mammals*, 1952.

Crowcroft, Peter, *The Life of the Shrew*, 1957.   *Species*

Darling, F. Fraser, *A Herd of Red Deer*, 1937.

Godfrey, Gillian, and Crowcroft, Peter, *The Life of the Mole*, 1960.

Lockley, R. M., *The Seals and the Curragh*, 1954.

Neal, Ernest, *The Badger*, 1948.

Shorten, Monica, *Squirrels*, 1954.

Page, F. J. Taylor, *Field Guide to British Deer*, 1959.

Perry, Richard, *The Watcher and the Red Deer*, 1952.

Thompson, Harry V., and Worden, Alastair N., *The Rabbit*, 1956.

BIRDS

Armstrong, E. A., *The Folklore of Birds*, 1958.   *General*

Bannerman, David A., *The Birds of the British Isles*, 1953 (ten out of twelve volumes published).

Campbell, Bruce, *Birds in Colour*, 1960.

Coward, T. A., *The Birds of the British Isles and their Eggs*, 7th edition, 1950.

Fisher, James, *Bird Recognition*, 1947– (three out of four volumes published).

Fitter, R. S. R., *The Pocket Guide to British Birds*, 1961.
The Pocket Guide to Nests and Eggs, 1959.
Hollom, P. A. D., *The Popular Handbook of British Birds*, 1952.
The Popular Handbook of Rarer British Birds, 1960.
Nicholson, E. M., *Birds and Men*, 1951.
Peterson, Roger, Mountfort, Guy, and Hollom, P. A. D., *A Field Guide to the Birds of Britain and Europe*, 1962.
Witherby, H. F., Jourdain, F. C. R., Ticehurst, C. B., and Tucker, B. W., *The Handbook of British Birds*, 1938–41.

Species   Armstrong, Edward A., *The Wren*, 1955.
Buxton, John, *The Redstart*, 1950.
Fisher, James, *The Fulmar*, 1952.
Fisher, James, and Lockley, R. M., *Sea-Birds*, 1954.
Lack, David, *The Life of the Robin*, 1953.
Swifts in a Tower, 1956.
Lockley, R. M., *Puffins*, 1953.
Shearwaters, 1942.
Lowe, Frank A., *The Heron*, 1954.
Mountfort, Guy, *The Hawfinch*, 1957.
Nethersole-Thompson, Desmond, *The Greenshank*, 1951.
Smith, Stuart, *The Yellow Wagtail*, 1950.
Snow, D. W., *A Study of Blackbirds*, 1958.
Spencer, K. G., *The Lapwing in Britain*, 1953.
Tinbergen, Niko, *The Herring Gull's World*, 1953.

REPTILES AND AMPHIBIANS
Smith, Malcolm, *The British Reptiles and Amphibians*, 1951.

FISHES
Jenkins, J. Travis, *The Fishes of the British Isles*, 1942.
Jones, J. W., *The Salmon*, 1959.
Kenyon, Ley, *Pocket Guide to the Undersea World*, 1956. (Chapter 7.)
Regan, C. Tate, *British Freshwater Fishes*, 1911.

INVERTEBRATES
Bristowe, W. S., *The World of Spiders*, 1958.
Cloudsley-Thompson, J. L., *Spiders, Scorpions, Centipedes and Mites*, 1958.

Cloudsley-Thompson, J.L., and Sankey, John, *Land Inverte-brates*, 1961.

Free, John B., and Butler, Colin G., *Bumble-bees*, 1959.

Imms, A.D., *Insect Natural History*, 1947.

Sankey, John, *Guide to Field Biology*, 1958.

Savory, T.H., *The World of Small Animals*, 1955.

    The Spider's Web, 1952

4 The Habitats of Wildlife

One of the first things the naturalist or nature lover notices as he goes about the countryside is how the types of animal and plant he encounters vary according to the nature of the country. Indeed, it is changes in the major plant communities, from grass, say, to heather moor, or from birch heath to oak woodland, that produce the major outwardly visible changes in the appearance of the countryside, although of course it is usually changes in the nature of the rocks which underlie these changes in vegetation.

The habitats of animals and plants can be broadly divided into three categories: land, waterside, and water. Terrestrial habitats can be further subdivided into those that are completely artificial, such as built-up areas, including houses with gardens, waste ground, and farmland, and those that are semi-natural, such as woodland, downs, heaths, moors, and mountains. The waterside habitats comprise both the freshwater bogs, fens, marshes, and lake and riversides, and the seaside cliffs, dunes, saltmarshes, and beaches. The water habitats can also be divided into freshwater and marine, with brackish water forming an intermediate category.

LAND HABITATS

To the majority of people the most familiar habitats for wildlife are those which are completely artificial; the towns, villages, and suburbs where they themselves live. A remarkable number of animals and plants have successfully adapted themselves to living in our midst; many of them indeed are among our most unwelcome pests and weeds. Even indoors we find in many older houses fungi, such as the dreaded dry-rot, moulds, rats, mice, and a wide range of insect pests, such as cockroaches, silver-fish, and house-crickets. Several birds, including

starlings, jackdaws, swifts, house martins, barn owls (Fig. 36), *36. Barn owls*
and feral pigeons, nest on or in old buildings, the martins
characteristically with their mud nests affixed to the walls just
under the eaves. Starlings roost on buildings in many large
towns, including London, Birmingham, Manchester, and Newcastle upon Tyne. Bats, too, roost in old buildings, not just in
belfries, as well as more naturally in caves and hollow trees.

As soon as stone walls or buildings start to become ruinous,
they provide an admirable home for many wild flowers, such
as wall pennywort (Fig. 37). Ludlow Castle walls, for instance,
are hanging gardens full of snapdragon, wallflower, greater
celandine, feverfew, wall rocket, red valerian, marjoram, and
harebell, among others. A survey of 500 old walls in Middlesex
showed that over 200 different species of wild plant were growing on them. Many of these wall-loving plants also grow on
waste ground, such as the fast-vanishing bombed sites of the
City of London, where in the past twenty years nearly 300
different species have been found growing. The brilliant dis-

plays of the yellow Oxford ragwort and the purple rose-bay willowherb (often mistaken for loosestrife) have heartened many a City worker hurrying to his office. Both ragwort and willowherb have brought attractive insects to the City: the red-and-black cinnabar moth, whose black-and-yellow caterpillar feeds on the ragwort, and the elephant hawkmoth, whose horned caterpillar eats the leaves of rose-bay. The City bombed sites also have their special bird, the robin-like black redstart, a newcomer to Britain since 1923, which now nests regularly in crevices in old buildings and elsewhere in several towns in the south of England.

All our larger towns are surrounded by a broad belt of houses with gardens, interspersed with parks and other open spaces. Whereas house sparrows and feral pigeons are almost the only birds which breed in the inner, completely built-up zone, the garden belt has been colonized by a good selection of woodland birds, notably blackbirds, song and mistle thrushes, starlings,

*37. Wall
pennywort*

robins, hedgesparrows, wrens (Fig. 38), chaffinches, great and blue tits, and spotted flycatchers. In a recent survey of the bird life of an area of almost a square mile of houses with small gardens in north London, Eric Simms found twenty-one regular breeding species. To these birds houses with gardens appear as inland cliffs and crags scattered among open woodland and scrub, for most gardens are well stocked with small trees and bushes. The commoner garden butterflies are the two cabbage whites, the small tortoiseshell, whose caterpillars feed on the nettle patch over the garden hedge, and the migratory red admiral and painted lady. Wild plants naturally do not get much of a chance in most gardens, but daisies, dandelions, and ribwort plantains are well-known weeds of lawns, while groundsel, red deadnettle, and shepherd's purse grow in the more neglected flower-beds and kitchen gardens.

The greater part of the ordinary green countryside of Britain is cultivated farmland, which falls broadly into two categories: grassland and arable or ploughland, with the dividing hedge-

38. Wren's nest in a bundle of nets hanging in a garden shed

rows as a third category that is vitally important to the wildlife, for they form the chief remaining reservoirs of many species of both animal and plant over wide tracts of country. Grass-land can be divided on the one hand into a rapidly diminishing amount of semi-natural permanent meadow or pasture, rich in interesting wild flowers, such as fritillary, meadow saffron, and green-winged orchid, and the now almost universal grass ley, which is regularly ploughed and resown with artificial mixtures of grass and clover seed. In many districts the only semi-natural grassland remaining lies in strips along the head-lands of both grass and arable fields and on the roadsides, where such plants as meadow cranesbill and birdsfoot trefoil provide a gay show in spring and summer. This is why naturalists attach such importance to the prevention of unnecessary spray-ing of roadsides with weedkiller. Grassland in permanent pastures and meadows and on road verges can be further classi-fied according to whether it lies over acid, neutral, or basic soil, for the typical grasses and other herbs of these three types vary considerably. The fine tall brome grass *Bromus erectus*, for instance, grows on roadsides almost exclusively on chalk and limestone, in districts where the roadside trees tend to be ash rather than oak or elm.

By its very nature, arable land can offer homes only to weeds, mostly annuals, though a few, such as the field bindweed, are tenacious deep-rooted perennials. A combination of cleaner seed-corn and intensive application of weedkillers has brought an end to the days when cornfields might be blue with corn-flowers or purple with corn-cockle; even fields red with poppies or yellow with charlock are now scarce. Such rarer cornfield weeds as pheasant's eye *Adonis annua* and thorow-wax or hare's ear *Bupleurum rotundifolium* now make a red-letter day for the botanist when he finds a farmer who has let them grow.

The commonest hedgerow plant is the hawthorn, but many other shrubs and innumerable attractive wild flowers, such as greater stitchwort, tufted vetch, lords and ladies (Fig. 39), and wild roses find refuge there and adorn the wayside. From

39. Lords and ladies (*wild arum*)

40. Lapwing on its nest in a marshy meadow

April to July many hedge-banks are white with a succession of umbellifers, first the common cow parsley *Anthriscus sylvestris*, followed in late May by the rough chervil *Chaerophyllum temulentum*, and in early July by the hedge parsley *Torilis japonica*, while on the grass roadside nearby hogweed *Heracleum sphondylium* flowers from late spring through to the verge of winter.

It is the hedgerows that give variety to the bird life of farmland. Few birds would nest in hedgeless fields except partridges, lapwings (Fig. 40), skylarks, and in some districts corn buntings. The hedges give shelter to many of the garden birds, and to two birds especially characteristic of the English country lane, but rarely seen in gardens, the yellowhammer and the whitethroat. The hedgerow trees also bring in nesting rooks, carrion crows, and magpies, among others. In winter large flocks of birds, not all of them welcome to the farmer, feed in his fields; among them rooks, jackdaws, lapwings, starlings, woodpigeons, skylarks, and in some favoured districts, such as the Yorkshire and Lincolnshire wolds, grey geese. Moles (Fig. 41), though rarely seen, are typical mammals of farmland.

Two thousand years ago the greater part of the British Isles was covered with woodland, so that in some sense woodland can be considered the most natural habitat of Britain. However, virtually none of our existing woodland is really natural; all has been interfered with by man in greater or less degree. The major division in our woodland is between broad-leaved and coniferous woods, and by far the greater part of our coniferous woodland consists of artificial plantations, mainly of Scots pine, larch, spruce, and various North American conifers. The ground flora of these is of negligible interest. In the three dozen or so surviving native Scots pinewoods in the Highlands, however, such as Rothiemurchus on Speyside and the Black Wood of Rannoch, there are such interesting specialities as twinflower *Linnaea borealis* and chickweed wintergreen *Trientalis europaea*, together with such commoner plants as bilberry, cowberry *Vaccinium vitis-idaea*, and juniper.

The majority of our broad-leaved woods are oakwoods, with a greater or less admixture of ash. The oakwoods of the heavier soils of the south and east are mostly of pedunculate oak *Quercus robur*, and those of the northern and western hills more often of the durmast oak *Q. petraea*. Ashwoods grow mostly on the Carboniferous Limestone in the Mendips, Derbyshire, and elsewhere, beechwoods on the Cotswolds and the south-eastern Chalk, and birchwoods in the Highlands or on southern heaths. Each type of woodland has its characteristic ground flora. Coppiced oakwoods often have magnificent displays of such spring carpeters as primroses, bluebells, and wood anemones, which are able to flower before the leaves are on the trees. This transitional type of oakwood, with standard oaks spaced out among an underwood mainly of hazel, was devised in the early Middle Ages to provide both oak for timber and hazel for wattle and hurdles. Though based on the natural forest it is in fact quite artificial and is now dying out. Beechwoods have a duller ground flora in spring, mostly wood sanicle and dog's mercury, but by way of compensation an especially rich array of fungi in autumn and two interesting saprophytes (plants which live on rotting vegetation), the birdsnest orchid *Neottia nidus-avis*, and the yellow birdsnest *Monotropa hypopitys*. Birchwoods are often adorned by the handsome red-and-white fly agaric, a poisonous toadstool.

Woods have a rich insect fauna, dependent on their distinctive floras, for most of the larvae are specialized feeders. The woodland butterflies are especially attractive, and there are few finer sights than a woodland glade in July where silver-washed or high brown fritillaries are sunning themselves on the tall marsh thistles, gliding elegantly from one to another. Two smaller woodland butterflies are the green and purple hair-streaks, found only in oakwoods, for it is one of the many insects whose larvae feed on this universal provider among our trees. Some insects, such as the tiny green moth *Tortrix viridana*, love the oak all too well, for in some years their larvae will completely strip the trees of their leaves in May and June, so that they have to grow a second crop in the summer.

We have already met many of the woodland birds in the guise of garden birds, but others, such as the warblers and woodpeckers, the common redstart, marsh and long-tailed tits, nightingale, woodpigeon, pheasant, woodcock, and sparrow-hawk are seen only in the larger gardens. The commonest breeding birds of woodland generally are probably the black-bird, chaffinch, willow warbler, and blue tit. Coniferous woods, especially in Scotland, have their special avifauna, which includes crossbill, siskin, coal and crested tits, and capercaillie. In winter the woods are almost deserted by birds, except for wandering parties of tits, often accompanied by nuthatches and treecreepers, and for blackbirds, whose scrapings among the dead leaves on the woodland floor often sound like the footsteps of some much larger animal.

Most of what appears to be the wildest part of Britain, the open downs, moors, heaths, and mountains, is in fact just as artificial as the rest. Except on the highest mountains, above

the natural tree-line, all was once more or less wooded and has
been felled by man and prevented from reverting to woodland
by the grazing of his sheep and cattle, which have eaten down
the seedlings.

The downs and wolds are calcareous grasslands, formerly
kept open by sheep and rabbit grazing, but now rapidly reverting first to scrub and later to woodland. Their flora is one of the
glories of Britain's natural scene, gay from May to July with
orchids, rock-rose, clustered bellflower, carline thistle (Fig. 42),
birdsfoot trefoil, cowslip (Fig. 43), horseshoe vetch, greater
knapweed, and various yellow dandelion-like flowers, such as
the greater hawkbit *Leontodon hispidus*. There are special
butterflies to match, including the marbled white and three
or four kinds of blue, among them the brilliant adonis blue,
whose caterpillars feed on the horseshoe vetch, and the handsome pale blue chalkhill blue. The bird of the open downs is
the skylark, and local specialities include the stone curlew, the
quail, and where there are scattered trees, as on Salisbury
Plain, that attractive little falcon the hobby.

The lowland heaths of southern and eastern England, on the other hand, are all on acid soils, and so have a totally distinct flora, whose main feature is often ling heather *Calluna vulgaris* and purple bell-heather *Erica cinerea*, with the pink bell-heather *E. tetralix* growing in damper spots, where also in a fast-diminishing number of places can be found the handsome deep blue trumpets of the marsh gentian. Gorse and broom are both characteristic shrubs of south country heaths, though gorse occurs also on the chalk downs, like the grayling and dark green fritillary butterflies. The small heath butterfly also belies its name in not being confined to heaths; it flies on all kinds of grassland and its caterpillar feeds on various kinds of grass. Birds which are heathland specialities, though again not confined to that habitat, include the stonechat, nightjar, red-backed shrike, and the rare Dartford warbler, our only resident species of warbler. Common lizards are widespread on heaths all over Britain, but only on the heaths of Surrey, Hampshire, and Dorset does the rare smooth snake occur and

43. Cowslip

this is also the main area for its chief prey, the equally local sand lizard.

The northern moors differ from the southern heathlands chiefly in being higher and therefore colder and more treeless. Their characteristic plant is the ling heather and their special tree the rowan or mountain ash, though vast areas of moorland are in fact grassy or covered with bracken. The little yellow tormentil and blue or white milkwort are both typical of acre upon acre of otherwise rather dull moorland. The special moorland insects include the emperor moth with its handsome green and black heather-feeding caterpillar and the oak eggar and various other more or less remote relatives of the silkworm moth. All these eggars have furry caterpillars, beloved of the cuckoos which frequent the moors to parasitize the meadow pipits, which are by far the most abundant birds there. The red grouse is the other typical moorland bird, almost entirely dependent on heather for its food, while skylarks are common and such interesting birds as the ring ouzel, greenshank (Fig.

44. Green-shank removing eggshell from its nest on a Highland moor

45. Blue (or mountain) hare

44), twite, and merlin, become more frequent as you go north-wards. The blue hare (Fig. 45) is also typical of the moors of the eastern Scottish Highlands.

Moorland shades gradually into mountain, the heather thins out and eventually there is nothing but bare scree and boulders, and a harsh climate. Even up here there are special plants, such as the wild azalea *Loiseleuria procumbens*, the tiny willow *Salix herbacea*, our smallest native shrub, and various alpine sedges and rushes; a special butterfly, the mountain ringlet; and several special birds, the ptarmigan, which is the mountain grouse, the dotterel, a kind of plover, and sometimes the snow bunt-ing, which finds on the tops of some of the highest Scottish bens a climate similar to that of Greenland and Iceland, which it prefers.

WATERSIDE HABITATS

An increase in the moisture in the soil at once brings in a whole new range of animals and plants, whether the habitat is merely rather wet underfoot, is actually interspersed with pools of water, or lies on the margin of open water, such as a river or lake. Laymen apply the terms fen, bog, marsh, and swamp rather loosely to these wet habitats, but to ecologists they all have precise meanings. Marshes and swamps have inorganic, mineral soils; fens and bogs have organic, peaty soils. In a marsh the soil is only slightly waterlogged in summer, with the water-level normally at about ground level. In swamps, on the other hand, the water-level is normally a few inches above the surface of the ground even in summer; most swamps in Britain are dominated by tall grasses, sedges, or rushes, especially the common reed *Phragmites communis* which is a grass. The flora at the margins of rivers, streams, lakes, and ponds ranks as swamp vegetation. Fens have a vegetation very similar to marshes, and their soil may be anything from slightly acid to markedly alkaline. Bogs, on the other hand, have a very distinct flora, dominated by sphagnum mosses, and are always highly acid.

Most groups of flowering plants have their moist habitat specialists. Among the orchids, for instance, there are several species of marsh orchid (*Dactylorchis*) and the marsh helleborine; the campions produce ragged robin, the woundworts *Stachys palustris*, and the buttercups the greater and lesser spearworts and celery-leaved buttercup *Ranunculus sceleratus*. Others, such as grass of Parnassus, which is no grass but has a handsome white buttercup-like flower, and the flowering rush (Fig. 46) have no close dry-habitat relatives in Britain. The yellow flag is one of the more conspicuous and attractive wild flowers of marshes generally and also river and streamsides. The distinction between the flora of bogs and fens is very marked; for instance, each has its own special spotted orchid and cotton-grass, *Dactylorchis fuchsii* and *Eriophorum latifolium* in fens, and *D. maculata* and *E. angustifolium* in bogs, while several species, such as bog asphodel, the little yellow bog orchid, and the three sundews grow only in bogs. The sundews are of great interest as being among our few insect-eating plants, the unfortunate insects being caught on the sticky 'fly-paper' hairs of their leaves. Willows, sallows, poplars, and alders are the trees most commonly associated with riversides and other damp habitats.

Among mammals otters, water voles, and that large South American fur-farm escape now widespread in East Anglia, the coypu, all frequent watersides and gain part of their living in the water. Birds that frequent lowland fresh water in the breeding season include the kingfisher, which nests in holes in banks; the moorhen and water rail which nest in reed and other swamps; the reed warbler, which occurs almost exclusively in reed swamps, attaching its small deep nest to the stems of the reeds; and the sedge warbler and reed bunting, which frequent marshy places and watersides generally. Dippers, grey wagtails, and common sandpipers are especially associated with the upland streams of the north and west; and bearded tits and

46. Flowering rush

bitterns (Fig. 47) with the marshes and swamps of East Anglia. Freshwater margins, especially the exposed muddy shores of reservoirs, are favourite feeding places of waders on migration. A few butterflies and rather more moths are waterside specialists, among them the local marsh fritillary; the large heath, a northern butterfly, whose caterpillar feeds on the white beaksedge *Rhynchospora alba* which grows only in acid bogs; and a score of different species of wainscot moth. Dragonflies are the special glory of many of our watersides in summer.

By the sea again a quite different assemblage of animals and plants appears. The main types of habitat are sea cliffs, sand dunes, saltmarshes, shingle beaches, and grassy seawalls, each with their own speciality. Sea cliffs, for instance, offer homes to many attractive but rare or local plants, including two kinds of stock, and lovage (*Ligusticum*), a northern umbellifer that comes no farther south than Northumberland. Many grassy slopes by the sea afford magnificent spring displays of such woodland plants as primroses and bluebells, with the addition, in the west, of the spring squill, and on all coasts of seaside specialities such as thrift or sea pink and sea campion. Sea cliffs also offer safe nesting sites to two groups of birds: those that will also nest on inland crags, such as raven, carrion crow, jackdaw, kestrel, buzzard, and peregrine, and the exclusively marine guillemot, razorbill, puffin, kittiwake (Fig. 48), gannet, shag, and rock pipit. In between is a group that usually nests by the sea, but occasionally does so inland: cormorant, herring gull, and the two black-backed gulls. Most of the true sea-birds nest in colonies, and these can be quite spectacular in the breeding season, when several thousand individual birds of several different species are all present at once. The most accessible of the larger seabird colonies are on the Pembrokeshire islands of Skomer and Skokholm, the Farne Islands in Northumberland, the Bass Rock in the Firth of Forth, and Ailsa Craig in the Firth of Clyde; Handa off the coast of Sutherland is magnificent but less easy to reach.

Sand dunes are a great contrast with often only the marram grass which binds the sand together to provide any vegetation at all. But the older dunes have a grassy turf and a most interesting flora approximating to that of the chalk downs, while in between the dunes are often damp hollows called slacks, with a good marsh or fen flora. On parts of the east coast thickets of the sea-buckthorn (*Hippophae*), the special sand-dune shrub, make a brave show with their silvery leaves and orange berries in autumn. Still another group of plants, such as sea rocket *Cakile maritima* and saltwort *Salsola kali*, grows along the drift-line on sandy shores. The special birds of sand dunes are the terns (Fig. 49); five species breed in colonies in the British Isles, often in spectacular numbers, as

48. Guillemots
and kittiwakes
on the Farne
Islands

at Havergate Island in Suffolk, Blakeney Point and Scolt Head Island in Norfolk, and Drigg Point near Ravenglass in Cumberland. Sometimes they are accompanied by colonies of black-headed gulls which are, however, equally at home nesting on moors and bogs inland, and even on a swampy sewage farm in Middlesex within a stone's throw of London Airport. Skylarks and ringed plovers also nest regularly on sand dunes.

Shingle is a harsh environment for plants, but as it grows older mosses and lichens help to form some sort of soil over it, so that the more inland parts of the great shingle banks, such as Chesil Bank in Dorset, the Crumbles near Eastbourne, Dungeness on the Kent–Sussex border, and Orfordness in Suffolk, can offer displays of sea campion, sea holly, yellow horned poppy, sea kale, and other seaside plants. On Dungeness the shingle is old enough to have produced scrub of blackthorn and broom, with sallows coming in on the damper spots. In North Norfolk and a few other places will be found stands of the low Mediterranean shrub *Suaeda fruticosa*, into whose straggly shelter hundreds of migrant birds thankfully dive on arriving from across the North Sea each autumn. The

49. Common
terns

breeding birds of shingle are much the same as those of sand dunes.

Saltmarshes have another very specialized flora, mostly rather dull and unattractive to look at, except for the purple swathes of sea-lavender in late summer, though in the autumn marsh samphire *Salicornia* and other plants often turn bright red and afford a fine contrast with the silvery foliage of the sea purslane *Halimione portulacoides*. Perhaps the most striking change that has come about on our coasts in the past fifty years has been the creation of many new acres of saltmarsh as a result of the planting of the hybrid cord-grass *Spartina townsendii*. This can grow in very soft mud and has reclaimed huge areas of estuary that were formerly completely barren, for instance in the Solent and Bridgwater Bay. Many wading birds feed in the muddy runnels that divide the vegetated parts of saltmarshes.

WATER HABITATS

The wildlife of both fresh and salt water is so vastly different from that of the land and even of the waterside, that it is impossible here to give more than the briefest survey of its variety. This is inevitable because of the different ways of life involved. For instance, most animals living in water get their oxygen by breathing water instead of air and wholly submerged plants must contrive to get themselves fertilized under water. Then there is almost as wide a range of habitats both in fresh water and in the sea as there is on the land. But as this book is mainly concerned with the wildlife that can be seen by people walking about the country or by the sea, and many of these differences affect only animals and plants that are submerged and scarcely visible from the shore, these fascinating realms will for the most part have to be relegated to 'further reading', on which guidance is available on page 93.

Freshwater habitats range all the way from Loch Ness to the puddles in the town-hall car-park, but the most important ones are lakes and ponds, rivers and streams, all terms which have their special meanings. Roughly speaking, lakes are large and ponds are small, but many so-called lakes in town parks are biologically ponds, while ponds as large as Frensham Great Pond on the borders of Hampshire and Surrey would perhaps be more accurately described as lakes. True lakes are of two main kinds, eutrophic lowland lakes, which are rich in nutrients and small animal and plant life, e.g. the meres of Cheshire and Shropshire; and oligotrophic lakes, which are poor in nutrients and wildlife and usually found in the mountains, for instance Wastwater and Buttermere in the Lake District. There is no real biological dividing-line between a river and a stream, or, lower down the scale, between a brook or a rill; more important is the broad difference between the turbid lowland streams with their muddy bottoms and the clear upland ones which run over stones and rocky beds. In the latter the only fish are often brown trout.

Many fewer plants grow in than around fresh water, and different ones grow in still and moving water. Some pondweeds (*Potamogeton*), water-milfoil (*Myriophyllum*), and certain water buttercups, for instance, form long trailing stems that wave about in the faster streams; the broad-leaved pondweed *P. natans* and the yellow and white water-lilies, on the other hand, prefer still waters where their broad leaves can rest placidly on the surface. The larger lakes are often too deep to have any plants growing in the middle. In stagnant or very slow-flowing waters there may be completely floating plants, such as duck-weeds, frogbit, and the remarkable water soldier, which rises to the surface to flower and then sinks again. The animals of ponds are familiar to most of us from the jamjar days of our youth: tadpoles, newts, and sticklebacks, water beetles and caddis grubs, dragonfly larvae and water-boatmen. Only the water-boatmen, water-skaters, and whirligig beetles are much seen on the surface.

In ponds and other freshwater habitats the ecological relationships of animals and plants can be seen and studied more easily than in any other habitat within reach of the ordinary person. In quite a small pond, you can find all the major groups of the animal and plant kingdoms, excepting only the echinoderms (starfishes and sea-urchins). This is why ponds make such valuable training grounds for young naturalists and biologists.

The flora and fauna of the inshore waters of the sea are far more numerous than those of fresh water, and vary according to whether the beaches are sandy, shingly, or rocky and the sea bottom rocky, sandy, or muddy. Only one group of flowering plants, the eel-grasses or grass-wracks (*Zostera*), grow actually in the sea; the remaining plants are all seaweeds or marine algae, a few of them growing quite far up into the brackish zone on estuaries. Five main zones on the shore are distinguished by their typical seaweeds. The topmost one, normally only splashed by spray but briefly covered by the highest spring tides, has the green cotton-wool-like alga *Enteromorpha* in its pools. Then come a green seaweed zone, typified by the cabbage-like *Ulva*, and the zone of the brown wracks, *Fucus*, some of which have the small air bladders that children delight to pop; both these are normally covered at high tide and uncovered at low tide. Below this comes the *Laminaria* zone, with stout ribbon-like brown seaweeds, which are uncovered only the lowest spring tides. Lower still, and never uncovered at all, is a zone of red seaweeds.

Most of the animals of the shore can only be seen by getting your feet wet, but barnacles of various kinds, with limpets and other molluscs, cling to the intertidal rocks, and lugworms scatter their casts over many acres of sandy tidal bays; while peering into pools often produces the sight of sea-anemones with their tentacles unfurled or shrimps or blennies darting under a rock. More familiar still are the remains of sea creatures cast up along the tideline, whelks' egg cases, 'mermaids' purses' (the egg cases of skates and dogfish), elongated razor shells, cuttle-fish shells, and whole dead starfish and jellyfish, the last sometimes cast up in vast quantities after a storm.

Further Reading

GENERAL

Tansley, A.G., *The British Islands and their Vegetation*, 1939.

LAND HABITATS

Homes, R.C., and others, *The Birds of the London Area since 1900*, 1957.

Lousley, J.E., *Wild Flowers of Chalk and Limestone*, 1950.

Nicholson, E.M., *Birds and Men*, 1951.

Pearsall, W.H., *Mountains and Moorlands*, 1950.

Raven, John, and Walters, Max, *Mountain Flowers*, 1956.

WATERSIDE HABITATS

Hepburn, Ian, *Flowers of the Coast*, 1952.

Steers, J.A., *The Sea Coast*, 1953.

WATER HABITATS

Barrett, John, and Yonge, C.M., *Pocket Guide to the Sea Shore*, 1958.

Clegg, John, *The Freshwater Life of the British Isles*, 1952.

Eales, N.B., *The Littoral Fauna of Great Britain*, 1961.

Macan, T.T., and Worthington, E.B., *Life in Lakes and Rivers*, 1951.

Yonge, C.M., *The Sea Shore*, 1949.

5 The Natural History Movement in Britain

There have always been more amateur naturalists than professionals in Britain. This is a distinction we share with other Anglo-Saxon, Nordic, and Germanic countries, in contrast to the Latin and Celtic countries, where fewer people study and enjoy wild animals and plants for their recreation. In Britain at every week-end, summer and winter, hundreds of naturalists and nature lovers go out into the country, sometimes alone or with a few friends, sometimes in organized parties of twenty or more, on bird-watching expeditions throughout the year, on fungus forays in the autumn, and seeking wild flowers and insect life in spring and summer. During each week thousands attend indoor meetings and listen to lectures or watch films on a wide range of subjects, while millions watch the excellent nature programmes on both kinds of television. This increasing popularity of the study and enjoyment of wildlife is no flash in the pan; it is the culmination of 400 years of development.

The Renaissance, beginning at the end of the fifteenth century, produced within fifty years the first Englishman to merit the name of naturalist, William Turner, Dean of Wells in the reigns of Edward VI and Elizabeth I. Previous writers on natural history got most of their information from books, as often as not from Pliny or Aristotle, but Turner was a field observer, and when he says he saw cranes or spoonbills nesting in East Anglia, we can believe him. Curiously enough he established a botanic garden at his home at Kew, some 200 years before the Royal Botanic Gardens were founded there. Turner was one of the first of the numerous herbalists of the sixteenth century, who were the first British field botanists. The herbalist best known to later generations is John Gerard the barber-surgeon.

The mid seventeenth century saw the real beginnings of

modern science, with the foundation of the Royal Society in 1663. This was for many years the only organized national society studying natural history as a whole. The greatest naturalist of this century, indeed still the greatest English naturalist after Darwin, was John Ray, a Cambridge don, who pioneered not only the study of the distribution of British animals and plants in the field, but also the classification of plants as a whole. In 1879 T.H.Huxley defined the three stages of biological knowledge:

Every country boy possesses more or less information respecting the plants and animals which come under his notice, in the stage of common knowledge; a good many persons have acquired more or less of that accurate, but necessarily incomplete and un-methodized knowledge, which is understood by Natural History; while a few have reached the purely scientific stage and, as Zoologists and Botanists, strive towards the perfection of Biology as a branch of Physical Science.

If Turner lifted the study of our wildlife from the stage of common knowledge to that of natural history, John Ray marks the beginning of its further transformation to biology.

The first half of the eighteenth century marked the beginning on the one hand of specialization, with the foundation of societies for naturalists primarily interested in plants or insects, and on the other of the local natural history society, with the appearance of philosophical clubs where country gentlemen could meet together to discuss interesting natural phenomena of all kinds. Many of the early societies and clubs were short-lived, petering out when the influence of the first secretary or president was removed. Both the botanists and the entomologists had several false starts, the botanists getting away first with Dillenius's Botanical Society, which lasted for only five years from 1721. The present Botanical Society of the British Isles dates its continuous ancestry from the Botanical Society of London, founded in 1836. The Royal Entomological Society also had several ephemeral ancestors before its continuous history began in 1833. One of these, the Aurelian

Society, was the first entomological society in the world, so far as is known. It was in existence in 1745, but came to an untimely end three years later when the great fire of Cornhill destroyed its library and collections, and the members themselves barely escaped with their lives. There was a second Aurelian Society in the 1760s, followed by a short-lived Society of Entomologists of London in the 1780s, and a third Aurelian Society in the early years of the nineteenth century. This society virtually committed suicide by imposing a rule that every member was obliged to fill gaps in the Society's own collection by presenting at least one specimen of every native insect he possessed. There were two more false starts before the present society was successfully launched at a meeting held in the British Museum in May 1833.

Meantime efforts had begun to found a national society devoted to natural history in general. On 21 October 1782 the short-lived Society for Promoting Natural History was born 'at Mr Dean's, the Corner House by the Turnpike, Pimlico'. While it was still drifting towards extinction, a group of dissatisfied members founded the Linnean Society of London, at the Marlborough Coffee House in Great Marlborough Street, on 26 February 1788. This society still exists as the premier general natural history society of the United Kingdom, having in 1829 acquired the collections of the great Swedish naturalist Linnaeus, in whose honour it was named, and in 1856 moved into its present rooms in Burlington House, which was bought by the Government especially to provide accommodation for learned societies.

The great name of the eighteenth century is that of Gilbert White, the quiet country parson who was the first amateur field naturalist in the modern style. White achieved fame for himself and his beloved Hampshire village, set in a fold of the downs, by carefully noting down the day-to-day facts of its natural history for thirty-five years and then writing a minor classic, *The Natural History of Selborne*. Published in 1788, this has become one of the most famous books in the English-speaking world, and for more than a century after it appeared it averaged at least one new edition every year. Selborne has changed relatively little since White wrote, and you can still see stinking hellebore and birdsnest orchid in its Hanger (hangers are woods that 'hang' on the side of a hill), autumn gentian on the open down, and golden saxifrage in the hollow lanes, just where he described them. Among White's more notable contributions to knowledge were the discovery of two new British mammals, the harvest mouse and the noctule bat; the separation of our three species of leaf warbler, the chiff-chaff, willow warbler, and wood warbler; and some observations on the life history of the field cricket which were not superseded until 1945.

After the entomologists and botanists had led the way by founding national societies in the 1830s, other branches of natural history were rather slow to follow suit. However, the British Ornithologists' Union was founded in 1858, and the Conchological Society in 1874, followed by a burst of activity in the 1890s when the present national societies dealing with mosses, ferns, fungi, and molluscs were founded. Apart from the creation in 1904 of the British Vegetation Committee, which became the British Ecological Society nine years later, a lull ensued till after the Second World War. Since then national societies dealing with reptiles and amphibians (1947), seaweeds (1952), mammals (1954), and lichens (1958), have been founded. Most of these are still largely run by and for amateur naturalists, but there is another large group of societies, mainly run by and for professional zoologists and botanists, including the Association for the Study of Animal Behaviour, the Association of Applied Biologists, and the Society of Experimental Biologists. Between the wars an important trend towards field natural history research developed, and, as some of the older national societies had become too wedded to the museum, library, and laboratory, new bodies were founded. The classic instance was the foundation in 1933 of the British Trust for Ornithology as the organization devoted to field research on British birds, leaving museum work and the study of birds overseas to the British Ornithologists' Union. In entomology there are two bodies now primarily concerned with field research, the Amateur Entomologists' Society (1935) and the British Trust for Entomology (1956). The botanists, though they hived off their ecologists as early as 1913, went on later in the century to absorb field work more successfully into the framework inherited from their founders.

To return to the other and in many ways more important half of the natural history movement, it was in the second quarter of the nineteenth century that the philosophical discussion clubs began to crystallize into local natural history societies as we know them today. Many of our older established county natural history societies and field clubs date from this seminal period, which also saw the birth of the Zoological Society of London and the national botanical and entomological societies which survive today: the Ashmolean Natural History Society of Oxfordshire was founded in 1828, the Natural History Society of Northumberland, Durham, and Newcastle upon Tyne in 1829, and the Berwickshire Naturalists' Club in 1831. During the 1840s, among others, the Cotteswold Naturalists' Field Club and the county societies for Somerset and Worcestershire were born. The movement gathered strength as the century wore on, and the vigorous activity of the early 1860s is reflected in the number of centenaries celebrated during the past three years, including those of major societies in Bristol, Devonshire, Dumfries and Galloway, and Yorkshire. There was another burst of new foundations in the 1870s and 1880s, after which pretty nearly the whole of England and large parts of Wales, Scotland, and Ireland were covered by a network of local societies, some for whole counties, others for towns or districts, and often catering for archaeologists as well as naturalists. The process has continued down to the present day, sometimes by way of revival, sometimes by filling a remarkable gap, sometimes by way of a completely new development, such as the foundation of local ornithological societies, devoted to bird watching alone, which began with the Oxford Ornithological Society in 1921. Even the past five years or so have seen the foundation of a new field club for the county of Kent, an ornithological society for the county of Sussex, and local natural history societies for Loughborough in Leicestershire, Uckfield in Sussex, and Wantage in Berkshire, among other places. Since 1956, too, virtually the whole of England and most of Wales has been covered by a network of county naturalists' trusts, whose work is described in Chapter 8. Today indeed there are hardly any districts and very few towns of any size in the United Kingdom where naturalists and nature lovers generally cannot find some local society, field club, naturalists' trust, or local branch of the British Naturalists' Association, where they can meet their fellows.

Until very recent years there has been no central body representing the natural history movement as a whole. At various times in the past such bodies as the Linnean Society, the British Naturalists' Association, and the Society for the Promotion of Nature Reserves appeared from their aims and objects to be aspiring to this status, but in the event they did not develop in this way. It was not until 1957 that discussions began to take place, under the auspices of the S.P.N.R., which led to the foundation of the Council for Nature, the body which now occupies this central position. The Council was founded at two meetings, appropriately held in the Linnean Society's rooms, in February and July 1958, and enjoyed from the start the royal patronage of the Duke of Edinburgh. It is a federal body, with corporate members only, though private individuals are welcomed as subscribers. At the time of writing (October 1962) the Council has 336 members, of whom 292 are natural history societies (54 national, 220 local, and 18 school or college), 17 naturalists' trusts, 21 museums, and 6 universities. These are all listed in the Appendix on page 169. Allowing for overlapping memberships, the Council's member societies are estimated to have more than 80,000 individual naturalist members.

The main aim of the Council for Nature is to represent the

natural history movement as a whole, wherever it is necessary to make the voices of naturalists and country lovers heard in public affairs. Since these occasions most often arise over some problem of conservation, this aspect of the Council's activities, together with its sponsorship of the Conservation Corps, is discussed in Chapters 8 and 9. As a result of generous grants of £5,000 a year for five years from the B.B.C., the Council has been enabled to run an Intelligence Unit, which began operations in May 1959 and has since acted as an information bureau on all questions relating to natural history and wildlife in the British Isles. The Unit also produces a duplicated monthly press bulletin for journalists and broadcasters and edits the Council's half-yearly printed bulletin, *News for Naturalists*.

From the beginning the Intelligence Unit has had a Films Officer, who has been available to advise amateur still and ciné photographers interested in photographing or filming wildlife. He has run a number of day and residential training courses, and as a result of the first of these the Nature Ciné Club was founded to fill a remarkable gap in the societies catering for naturalists. During 1960 the Council, jointly with the B.B.C., held a prize competition for natural history films, which was won by Messrs G. H. Thompson and R. Skinner of the Oxford University Forestry Department, with *The Life History of the Alder Woodwasp and its Insect Enemies*. The prize of £500 was presented by the B.B.C.

During 1961 the Council opened Brantwood, John Ruskin's old home in the Lake District, as a conference and holiday centre for naturalists, by arrangement with the Education Trust Ltd and its chairman Mr R. G. Lloyd. Brantwood can accommodate thirty people and ran a full programme of courses and conferences in both 1961 and 1962. Another service for naturalists offered by the Council is the administration of a fund set aside by the Carnegie United Kingdom Trust, from which grants can be made to local societies which need expert assistance for their field work. The first three grants were made to the Suffolk Naturalists' Society for the study of three populations of noctule bats; to the Selborne Society for the survey of their bird sanctuary at Perivale, Middlesex; and to Castleford and District Naturalists' Society for a study on a roost of swallows and martins at Fairburn Ings in Yorkshire.

The culmination of the Council's five years' work is National Nature Week, which it is organizing from 18 to 25 May 1963. There will be a major exhibition at the Royal Horticultural Society's halls in London, other exhibitions at important centres outside London, and special activities by many natural history societies throughout the country. The Council offered a prize of £50 for a suitable emblem for National Nature Week, and the prizewinning design, illustrated here, was by Michael Renton.

In addition to the 215 local natural history societies in membership of the Council for Nature, with a few more small ones which have not yet joined, there is now a wide range of national natural history societies with specialized functions. The Field Studies Council, for instance, founded as a wartime act of faith in 1943, now has six residential field centres where some ten thousand students come every year to attend courses, mainly on biological and geographical subjects, in the field. Some 1,250 of these students are amateur naturalists, the rest coming mainly from the sixth forms of the grammar schools, but with an important contingent from universities and training colleges. The six field centres are widely scattered through

England and Wales; Dale Fort in Pembrokeshire, Flatford Mill in Suffolk, Juniper Hall in Surrey, Malham Tarn in Yorkshire, Preston Montford in Shropshire, and Slapton Ley in Devon. The Scottish Field Studies Association also runs a field centre, in Glen Lyon, Perthshire.

Natural history societies for young people form a world of their own, and probably many more exist in various parts of the country than have become generally known. The leading ones include the Junior Bird Recorders Club, run by the Royal Society for the Protection of Birds; the XYZ Club, run by the Zoological Society of London; and the British Junior Naturalists' Association, run from the Scarborough Museum. These and others join together in a committee which coordinates young British naturalists in relation to the activities of the International Youth Federation for the Study and Conservation of Nature, which runs an annual camp in some part of Europe. There are also many junior sections of adult societies, both national and local: among them the British Naturalists' Association and the local societies for Banbury, Bristol, Cardiff, Darlington, Letchworth, Lincolnshire, London, Mid-Somerset, North Staffordshire, and South Essex. Many other local societies run special activities, such as prize essay competitions and camping week-ends, for their young members, and almost all of them have special junior membership subscriptions. The Middle Thames Natural History Society, for instance, has competitions for essays, illustrations, nature diaries, and wild-flower collections, and the Suffolk Naturalists' Society, besides an essay competition, includes a special schools supplement in its *Transactions*.

In addition there are innumerable school and college natural history societies, and on a national scale the School Natural Science Society, formerly the School Nature Study Union, whose members are mostly interested teachers, and the Association of School Natural History Societies, whose sixty-seven members are mainly at grammar and public schools. However, there are many more than this number of school societies in existence; well over 200 are known and at least another 100 probably exist in schools all over the country. The societies in membership of the Council for Nature are listed in the Appendix. There are also at least thirty-five, and probably half as many again, natural history societies at universities and teachers' training colleges.

There are remarkably few national journals in Britain which cover natural history in general. Those few include the Council for Nature's *News for Naturalists*, the British Naturalists' Association's *Country-Side*, and for young people *The Young Naturalist* (British Junior Naturalists' Association) and the *Wild Life Observer*. Most societies have transactions, proceedings, or reports of some kind, but there are four regional journals of a rather wider appeal: *The Naturalist*, which covers the North of England (Yorkshire Naturalists' Union), *Nature in Wales* (West Wales Naturalists' Trust), the *Scottish Naturalist*, the *Irish Naturalist's Journal*, and the *Field Naturalist*, covering North-West England. The last two are both produced by consortia of local societies. There are also a great many specialized journals, of which those of more general national interest include *British Birds*, the *Zoo Magazine* (X Y Z Club), and the *Junior Bird Recorder* (J.B.R.C.); and of local or regional interest *Scottish Birds* (Scottish Ornithologists' Club) and *Devon Birds* (Devon Bird Watching and Preservation Society).

No small part of the great postwar upsurge in interest in Britain's wildlife has been due to the excellent sound and television programmes put out by the B.B.C. and more recently also by I.T.V. The B.B.C.'s Natural History Unit at Bristol was founded in 1957 as a logical extension of the West Region's special interest in wildlife and country programmes, dating back at least as far as 1946, when the first edition of 'The Naturalist' went out. Audiences of anything up to six or seven millions now watch the leading B.B.C. television nature programmes, such as 'Look'.

The official body concerned with wildlife in Great Britain is the Nature Conservancy, set up by Royal Charter in 1949.

Since most of its work is concerned with conservation, it will be discussed in more detail in Chapter 8. Here, however, it may be mentioned that the Conservancy keeps close liaison with working naturalists, especially through its botanical and ento-mological liaison committees and the contacts maintained by its regional officers with both local societies and individual naturalists. The Conservancy is also closely concerned with biological and physiographical research into British wildlife and its habitats, not only through its own research stations, but also by grants given to private and university research workers. During 1960-1, for instance, grants were given for, among other projects, the experimental enclosure of an area of lime-stone pavement against grazing animals; the study of the accretion of beaches at Scolt Head, Norfolk; research into the pied flycatcher and the mountain hare; ringing grey seals on the north-east coast of England; and the study of butterfly populations on Kentish downland.

The Conservancy now maintains six research, experimental, or field stations, which cover a wide range of terrestrial habi-tats: Anancaun Field Station, Kinlochewe, Wester Ross; Furzebrook Research Station, Wareham, Dorset; Merlewood Research Station, Grange-over-Sands, Lancashire; Monks' Wood Experimental Station, near Huntingdon; Moor House Field Station, near Alston, Cumberland; and Speyside Re-search Station, near Aviemore, Inverness-shire.

Freshwater research is catered for by the Freshwater Bio-logical Association's Laboratory at Far Sawrey on Lake Windermere and by the Brown Trout Research Laboratory at Pitlochry, Perthshire. Marine biological research is even better provided for with the famous Plymouth Laboratory of the Marine Biological Association of the United Kingdom, the Millport Station of the Scottish Marine Biological Association on Great Cumbrae, Buteshire, the university marine biological laboratories at Port Erin, Isle of Man, and Cullercoats, North-umberland, and the Government ones at Aberdeen, Lowestoft, and Bangor, North Wales.

Further Reading

Gage, A. T., *A History of the Linnean Society of London*, 1938.

Lysaght, A., *Directory of Natural History and Other Field Study Societies in Great Britain*, 1959.

Neave, S. A., *The History of the Entomological Society of London, 1833–1933*, 1933.

Raven, C. E., *John Ray*, 1942.

English Naturalists from Neckam to Ray, 1947.

White, Gilbert, *The Natural History of Selborne*, Everyman ed., edited by R. M. Lockley, 1949.

6 Naturalists at Work

British amateur naturalists still play a remarkably large part in field research in botany and zoology. Not so long ago almost all field biological research was done by amateurs, the professionals concentrating on research in museums, libraries, and laboratories. The pioneer ecologists of the British Vegetation Committee, and Sir Julian Huxley in his path-breaking field study of the courtship behaviour of the great crested grebe fifty years ago, were among the first modern biologists to return to field work. Later, in the early 1930s, Huxley was one of the group of younger ornithologists who founded the British Trust for Ornithology, which is still the principal body concerned with field research on birds in the British Isles. The Trust quickly made its mark by organizing amateur bird watchers to take part in cooperative field inquiries. One of the earliest and most important of these was the Little Owl Inquiry, which demonstrated that the great bulk of the food of this introduced bird consisted of insects and small mammals, such as crane-flies, earwigs, beetles, field-mice, and voles. This helped to quieten the outcry which had arisen accusing the little owl of being a menace to game preservers.

For the past twenty-five years the principal research project of the Trust has been the Bird Ringing Scheme. Experimental bird ringing began in Britain in the 1890s, but large-scale ringing dates from 1909, when H. F. Witherby launched the parent of the present ringing scheme in connexion with his magazine *British Birds*. At the same time Dr (now Sir) Landsborough Thomson launched a ringing scheme at Aberdeen University, which lasted until the First World War. When Witherby handed over his ringing scheme to the British Trust for Ornithology in 1937, Thomson became, and has remained ever since, Chairman of the Trust committee which administers

*50. Ringing
a tree pipit*

it. Since 1937 the Ringing Scheme has been housed in the Bird
Room of the British Museum (Natural History) and its annual
report has continued to appear in *British Birds*. For many years
it was run largely by volunteer labour, with Miss E.P.Leach
as Hon. Secretary. In 1954, however, the Nature Conservancy
recognized the need to place this important work on a full-
time basis and made a substantial grant, which has continued,
to enable the present Secretary, Robert Spencer, and a full-
time staff to be engaged.

In 1960, the latest year for which figures are available at the
time of writing, 279,189 birds were ringed by more than 800
ringers. The process of ringing consists in putting a small num-
bered metal ring, bearing the legend 'Inform British Museum
Nat. Hist. London', on the bird's leg (Fig. 50). Birds to be
ringed may either be caught in various kinds of live traps or
in fine-meshed nets called mist-nets, or they may be ringed as
nestlings. In recent years, especially with the rise of mist-
netting as a method of catching birds, the Trust has recognized

that all and sundry cannot be allowed to ring birds without any training or guidance. A licensing system was introduced, and new ringers must now be trained by qualified ringers before they themselves are allowed to ring without supervision. Two possible dangers are thus averted: that the birds may be damaged when being extracted from the mist-nets and that the ring may be inefficiently put on the bird's leg.

Information of immense value has been gained as a result of bird ringing, even though fewer than 70,000 of the two and half million birds ringed since the beginning of the scheme have actually been recovered and reported back to the Ringing Committee. For instance, definite proof is now available of the winter quarters of our summer visitors and of the breeding places of our winter visitors: a good many British-ringed swallows have now been recovered in South Africa in the winter, while the black-headed gulls that visit the London area in winter are now known to breed in the Baltic, especially Denmark and Sweden. One individual gull was first caught in St James's Park in February 1939, caught there again in February 1945, and finally recovered in the Kattegat in June 1948. Ringing recoveries have also thrown a flood of light on the longevity and expectation of life of individual birds. Robins, for instance, have been proved to live for at least eleven years, despite the fact that the average expectation of life for an individual robin at any one time is only just over a year.

Besides the Ringing Scheme, the B.T.O. has three permanent inquiries and a number of short-term ones. The permanent ones include the nest-record scheme, which collects information on breeding biology at individual bird nests (Fig. 51), the sample census of heronries, and the roosting sites inquiry. The heron census has provided a continuous index of the heron population of Britain, which fluctuates around 4,500 breeding pairs, since the original national census organized by E. M. Nicholson in 1928. Its current short-term inquiries at the time of writing (October 1962) include a breeding-season census of common birds, inquiries into the

status and distribution of the peregrine, the stonechat, and the whooper swan, and a sample census of the mute swan, run in conjunction with the Wildfowl Trust. The common birds census is an important inquiry, undertaken at the request of the Nature Conservancy, to try to find some basis for assessing the effect of poisonous farm chemicals on bird life. Since the 1930s, when it was the most popular form of field bird research, census work on land birds has been relatively neglected, and it is interesting to see the Trust's wheel coming full circle again. The mute swan census is a follow-up of an earlier census which showed that there were some 15,000 mute swans in England and Wales in 1955 and a further 3,500 or so in Scotland.

The only other large-scale ornithological inquiry on a national basis is the Wildfowl Trust's national wildfowl counts, now carried out by a network of observers spread out over the whole country, who visit more than 500 of the larger inland waters and estuaries once a month, on the Sunday nearest to the 15th, and count all the ducks, geese, and swans they see. These counts have proved to be an invaluable source of information in assessing wildfowl stocks. Nearly 200,000 ducks may be counted in the peak winter period from November to January, including upwards of 80,000 wigeon, 60,000 mallard, and 30,000 teal. The research unit of the Wildfowl Trust also carries out aerial and other surveys of the distribution of various ducks, geese, and swans.

The Mammal Society of the British Isles has already surveyed the distribution of the brown hare and is currently engaged in surveying that of the badger. The Society's active Deer Group maintains a constant watch on the status and distribution of deer in the British Isles, including especially the three recently introduced and spreading species, sika, muntjac, and Chinese water-deer.

The British Herpetological Society announced at the end of 1960 a new survey of the distribution of British reptiles (snakes and lizards) and amphibians (frogs, toads, and newts), in which its members were invited to participate. The aim is to bring up to date the survey published in the Society's *Journal* for 1948.

The Distribution Maps Scheme of the Botanical Society of the British Isles, which has been substantially grant-aided by the Nature Conservancy, is perhaps the most ambitious scheme of research ever undertaken by a natural history society whose members are mainly amateurs. It is indeed believed to have been the most intensive survey of the distribution of flowering plants ever carried out in any part of the world. For three or four years from the summer of 1955 some 2,000 amateur botanists all over the British Isles were engaged in noting the occurrence in ten-kilometre squares of any native or naturalized flowering plant or fern. The British Isles were divided into some 3,500 of these squares, covering about thirty-six square miles each. In the event cards were received for all but ten of them, which were located in the Outer Hebrides, the Orkneys, and Central Ireland. The results of the scheme, which was directed first by Dr S. M. Walters, of Cambridge University Botany Department, and later by Dr Franklyn Perring, were published in June 1962 as *The Atlas of British Flora.*

The total number of plant records collected under the scheme was about a million and a quarter, and it is believed that this represents about three-quarters of the maximum possible number of records. The number of species on individual squares varied very widely. In parts of the south of England, where several different soils, such as chalk, sand, and clay all occurred on one square, up to 800 different plants might be found on it. On the other hand, in the Highlands of Scotland, where there is little cultivation and a uniform vegetation over extensive tracts of moorland, a square might produce no more than 120 species. The maps produced by the scheme throw an interesting light on which plants are really common (Figs. 52 and 53). Fewer than a dozen plants actually proved to occur literally in every ten-kilometre square in the British Isles: among them were ribwort plantain, self-heal, meadow, and creeping buttercups, and the grass curiously known as Yorkshire fog *Holcus lanatus.* Even the daisy is shown to be rare in some parts of Scotland. Many weeds common in the south, such as shepherd's purse, chickweed, and groundsel, are scarce in Scotland, where many of the wilder districts have little or no cultivated ground.

The British Naturalists' Association runs a Phenological Inquiry in which members note the earliest flowering of certain common wild flowers, such as coltsfoot and lesser celandine, and the appearance of bird migrants and butterflies.

The activities of local natural history societies are understandably on a much smaller scale than those of national bodies. They are concentrated more on meetings, both indoors and in the field. An analysis of the topics discussed by lecturers at indoor meetings, based on the most recent syllabuses of seventy

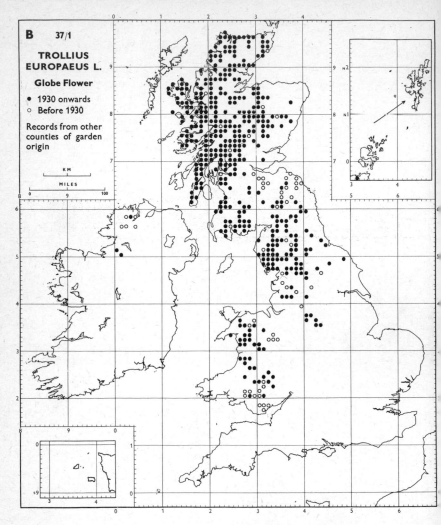

B 37/1

TROLLIUS
EUROPAEUS L.

Globe Flower

• 1930 onwards
○ Before 1930

Records from other
counties of garden
origin

KM

MILES
0   9   100

societies available in February 1962, shows that birds
are far and away the most popular subject. There were 131
bird films or lectures compared with only 40 for mammals and
other vertebrates, 67 for insects and other invertebrates, and
103 for all branches of botany. Foreign travel (74) and foreign
natural history (76) were also very popular lecture subjects.

*52. A distri-
bution map: t[...]
globe flower,
which grows
mainly in the
north*

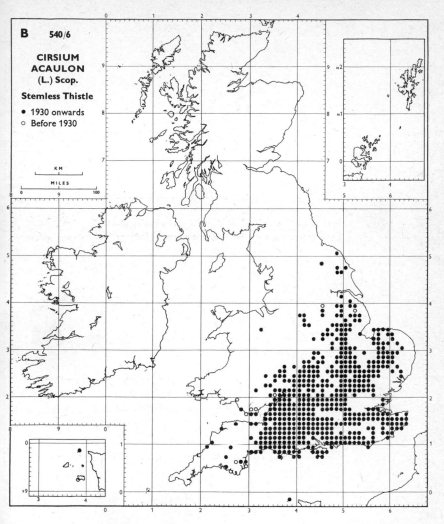

B 540/6

CIRSIUM
ACAULON
(L.) Scop.

Stemless Thistle

• 1930 onwards
○ Before 1930

KM

MILES

*53. A distri-
bution map: the
stemless thistle,
which grows
mainly in the
south*

Conservation was apparently somewhat neglected with only eleven periods specifically devoted to it. Most local societies meet once a month, except during the summer, but some meet throughout the year and larger ones may meet more frequently. The larger societies, such as London, Bristol, Suffolk, and Lincolnshire, may be split into sections, each catering for

113

special studies, such as ornithology, botany, and entomology, and this of course makes for more frequent meetings.

Though many members of local societies attend both indoor and field meetings, there is a certain tendency for some members to be mainly attracted by indoor meetings and others by field meetings. This is not wholly a division of the members by age, though naturally older members are more likely to prefer indoor meetings and younger ones outdoor meetings, but also to some extent reflects the division between the nature lover, who likes to be shown attractive pictures of wildlife, and the genuine naturalist, who likes to go out and see for himself. It may be of interest to show the field programme for a recent winter of a typical local society, the Middle Thames Natural History Society, based on Slough:

Sunday, 1 October. Silwood Park, Ascot. Fungi, bramblings, siskins, redpolls, etc. Meet at 'The Cannon', 10.30 a.m. Morning meeting only.

Saturday, 7 October. Bagshot and Swinley Heaths. Fungus Foray. Meet at Grid Reference 905650 on the main Ascot-Bagshot road at 2 p.m.

Saturday, 14 October. Virginia Water. Fungus Foray. Meet at the Wick Lane entrance at 11 a.m. Bring lunch.

Sunday, 9 November. Virginia Water. Wildfowl and winter visitors. Bring water-proof footwear! Morning meeting only. Meet at the entrance to the Wheatsheaf Hotel, 10.30 a.m.

Sunday, 18 February. Coach trip to the Wildfowl Trust, Slimbridge, Glos. Will all members wishing to go please notify the Secretary at least two weeks beforehand.

Summer programmes, of course, have many more meetings, and insects and wild flowers figure more prominently in the goals, but this short list well illustrates the flavour of local natural history society meetings. The concentration on Saturday and Sunday is noticeable; in summer there may be evening meetings to listen to nightjars and in May even all-night ones to hear the dawn chorus of bird song.

The prime purpose of most field meetings is to enable members to enjoy the countryside and its wildlife in the company of like-minded friends, and at the same time to familiarize themselves with the birds, wild flowers, and insects they encounter. Some societies, however, have field meetings on which they do serious scientific work, mainly ecological surveys. It was to encourage work of this kind that the Council for Nature persuaded the Carnegie United Kingdom Trust to offer the grants mentioned on page 100. Survey work is usually carried out with a single society, but in the Chilterns, which is a natural region divided among several different societies, a cooperative venture has been set up. This is the Chiltern Research Committee, representing eight local natural history societies and two naturalists' trusts in the counties of Bedford, Buckingham, Hertford, and Oxford. The Committee has launched cooperative inquiries into the status in the Chilterns of orchids, juniper, and wild candytuft *Iberis amara* among plants, and the woodlark, wood warbler, nuthatch, woodpeckers, and muntjac deer among animals.

Two societies ring grey seals as part of the Nature Conservancy's research programme into the population problems of this large marine mammal, which is protected by Act of Parliament. They are the Natural History Society of Northumberland, Durham, and Newcastle upon Tyne, which rings on the Farne Islands, and the West Wales Naturalists' Trust (formerly the West Wales Field Society), which rings on the coast of Pembrokeshire. The national bat-ringing scheme is organized through the Mammal Society.

A long-standing survey of a single area by a local society is that of Bookham Common in Surrey by the London Natural History Society. Started during the war, when travel difficulties brought to an end the Society's pre-war survey of Limpsfield Common in the same county, it has continued ever since. A great deal of information has been amassed about the birds, mammals, and flowering plants of the common (which consists partly of oakwood and partly of open grassy plains), and much also has been learned of various groups of invertebrates and lower plants. The Progress Report for the nineteenth year of the survey showed the following activities during 1960: listing of the plants of two areas of woodland for comparison with similar lists made in 1943; a census of the territories of singing males of certain birds in an area of dense oakwood; studies of the feeding niches of birds to try to find out how the encroachment of scrub on open grassland affects their feeding habits; collection of pellets from two roosting sites of barn owls to assess their food. Among the interesting facts reported was a decrease of breeding chaffinches in woodland to only one quarter of the population present in 1951; and the great predominance of field voles in the barn owls' diet (forty-three out of sixty-three small mammals present; there were also two birds, both hedgesparrows).

The same issue of the *London Naturalist*, and the concurrent one of the *London Bird Report*, the Society's two annual journals, carried papers reporting the results of a number of other surveys and individual research projects carried out by members. A selection from them will give some idea of the wide range of field natural history study possible in a large society (the L.N.H.S. with over 1,500 members is the largest local natural history society in Britain):

Notes on changes in the vegetation of Petersham Park, Surrey, since 1943, with a list of plants.

An analysis of the flowering plants and ferns of 500 walls in Middlesex.

A complete list of the mosses and liverworts of the London Area (a radius of twenty miles from St Paul's Cathedral).

The results of trapping for small mammals on Bookham Common.

The first report on a survey on the distribution of the stag beetle, which is commoner in the southern suburbs of London than anywhere else in Britain.

A preliminary list of the beetles of Farningham Wood, Kent.

A ten-year study on Headley Heath, Surrey, of the recolonization by plants of heathland denuded of topsoil by wartime army manoeuvres.

The vegetation of a sewage farm at South Norwood on the Kent–Surrey border.

Some notes on the geology of the Sutton district of Surrey.

Some notes on the snails and slugs of Devilsden Wood and the nearby downs, Coulsdon, Surrey.

A survey of the gull roosts of the Lea valley reservoirs.

An account of the London Migration Watch, when it was estimated that four million birds may have passed over London in seven autumn weeks.

A survey of the sand martin colonies of the London area.

An excellent example of the first-class work that can be achieved by a much smaller society is provided by the series of field inquiry reports issued by the East Lancashire Ornithologists' Club, centred on Burnley. These have included surveys of swift nesting sites, rook flight lines and winter roosts, the status of the chiffchaff and the twite, magpie roosts and the distribution of the house martin. The house martin report, by L. E. Bouldin and E. M. Jackson, shows a big increase in the number, both of nests and of colonies, in the area between 1958 and 1961. More than half the nests were built on private houses, one-third on barns and shippons, and the remainder on sheds or such public buildings as inns, hotels, schools, mills, chapels, churches, and police stations. Some three-quarters of all the nests were built on the fronts of buildings. The survey of swift nesting sites by K. G. Spencer revealed that the great majority were under eaves or in holes high up in the stonework of mills and houses built during the cotton boom years from 1850 to 1910.

Natural history is a sphere in which individual keen young people can produce research results fully as valuable and useful as those of their elders (Fig. 54). Two recent examples may be cited. N. B. Palmer, for instance, when attending Cheltenham Grammar School in 1958, studied the effect of disturbance on the times at which badgers emerge from their sets. He found

that at a completely secluded set in the Cotswolds badgers would appear some ninety minutes earlier than at another set not far away where they were subject to much disturbance such as children playing in the wood, pigeon shooting, and blocking of the set by the hunt. On one May evening the secluded badgers emerged only twenty minutes after sunset, but the other ones appeared two hours and twenty minutes later. These disturbed badgers would stand sniffing cautiously at the entrance for up to nine minutes before coming out, but the secluded ones might even trot straight out without a sideways glance.

54. Young botanists studying wild flowers in a meadow at Haslemere

An Essex schoolboy, M. R. Chettleburgh, was the first British ornithologist to make systematic observations on how jays bury acorns in the autumn. This he did in Hainault Forest in the autumn of 1951. He found, for instance, that the jays collected only from the part of the Forest where they were most abundant. They began in mid September and went on for two months, though there was a peak of activity around the middle of October, when there was a continuous stream of birds flying to and fro, each taking about ten minutes for the round trip from oak to burying place, which might be up to three-quarters of a mile away. About thirty-five jays were involved, and since each made six flights an hour during the ten hours from sunrise to sunset at the peak period, and carried three acorns at a time, they must have buried some 6,300 acorns during this ten days alone. The favourite hiding places were in small holes or niches in the ground under a thin covering of dead leaves. About a week after the burying ceased, jays started returning to their secret hoards and digging them up to feed on during the winter. They seemed to remember exactly where to look.

During the past thirty years an entirely new type of organization for natural history field work has come upon the scene. This is the bird observatory and field station, which began as a purely ornithological movement but developed into a wider interest in wildlife as a whole. The first two observatories were founded more or less at the same time in the mid 1930s by R. M. Lockley on the Pembrokeshire island of Skokholm, and by a group of young Edinburgh bird watchers on the Isle of May in the Firth of Forth. The May was already known to be a good place for studying bird migration, but to Lockley goes the credit for pioneering the movement which has shown the west coast of Britain to be just as interesting as the east coast in this respect. No other observatories were founded before the war, but soon after it a chain of observatories sprang up all round the coasts of the British Isles (see Appendix). On the east coast there are now Fair Isle, the Isle of May, Spurn Point, Gibraltar Point, Cley, Bradwell, and Dungeness; on the south coast Portland, Jersey, and St Agnes in the Scilly Isles; on the west coast Lundy, New Grounds, Skokholm, and Bardsey; and in Ireland Cape Clear Island, Copeland, Great Saltee, and Tory Island. Most of these observatories provide simple sleeping accommodation and cooking facilities for bird watchers and other naturalists who stay while making observations. Usually there is also a full-time warden to supervise and coordinate the individual observations. All the above observatories send representatives to the Bird Observatories Committee of the British Trust for Ornithology, which holds an annual conference in Oxford in January. Ornithological field work at the observatories is stimulated and coordinated by the Migration Research Officer of the Trust, Kenneth Williamson. A number of smaller observatories or ringing stations, including the Calf of Man, Sandwich Bay in Kent, and Walberswick in Suffolk, are not yet full members of the Committee. Quite lately there has also been a strong development towards inland bird observatories as well, and it seems likely that within five years or so there will be a further extensive network of observatories away from the coast. There is no doubt that this particular form of the new scientific sport of bird watching has come to stay. Probably well over 2,000 people spend at least one week at British and Irish bird observatories each year.

The ornithological research work carried out at the observatories consists mainly of visual observation of migrating birds, trapping and ringing of as many individuals as possible, and critical examination in the hand of the plumage of living birds. All observatories welcome workers from other branches of natural history, and most also have some speciality of their own. Thus Fair Isle has its long-term population studies of the great and arctic skuas, Bardsey specializes in marine biology and observations on birds killed at its lighthouse, and Lundy keeps track of the populations of its numerous colonies of seabirds. Skokholm Bird Observatory, which is run by the Field Studies Council as an adjunct to Dale Fort Field Centre, has a research project on the social structure in lesser black-backed gull colonies. In addition, during 1960 two Ministry of Agriculture scientists studied the rabbit population there, a Medical Research Council worker investigated the island's house mice, and a private research worker mapped the extent of bracken on a scale of twenty-five inches to the mile.

Further Reading

The Transactions, Proceedings, Journals, and Annual Reports of
the Societies concerned.

Ennion, Eric, *The House on the Shore*, 1960. (Monks' House Bird
Observatory.)

7 How to Observe Wildlife

Wildlife can be observed anywhere from the window of a block of flats in London to the top of Ben Nevis or the bottom of the sea off Bournemouth. All the basic equipment you need is a pair of sharp eyes and good ears, the patience to wait and watch, and the ability to keep silent. If you are walking in the countryside, walk slowly and quietly, but better still is to find some vantage point and stop or sit down. If you sit still anywhere in the countryside for half an hour, or even ten minutes, it is astonishing what you can see, especially in the way of birds. Most mammals are nocturnal, so you are less likely to see them. Ears are as important as eyes to the naturalist, and the experienced bird watcher probably detects as many of his birds by sound as by sight. The squeaking of mice and shrews and the high-pitched calls of grasshoppers and other insects can also readily be picked up by the silent wanderer in the countryside. Some creatures make remarkably loud non-vocal noises; to hear a hedgehog progressing through the undergrowth at night, you might think that an animal as large as a wolf was about.

It follows that one is the ideal number for an expedition to watch wildlife, unless you can provide yourself with companions who know when to keep quiet. One reason why reservoirs and estuaries are so popular for local natural history societies' field meetings is that water and waterside birds can often be identified at a distance by a party, who only have to be persuaded to keep quiet and creep up the bank of the sea wall and peep over. After that, on the way home, the social aspect of the meetings can flourish. This is where botanists have the advantage over bird watchers, for wild flowers and fungi are not frightened away by human voices, and all that is necessary is to ensure that the plants are not trampled on.

Many people find that it adds great pleasure to their watching of wildlife to keep notes and records, most often in the form of a diary. The Wild Flower Society prints special diaries for its members to record the first flowering of each plant in the spring, and runs competitions for those who see the largest number each year. The most important thing about keeping notes is to write them down as soon as possible, before you start to forget exactly what you saw, or see something else that puts the first observation out of your mind. So it is a great help always to carry a notebook and pencil with you, and to copy your field notes out into a more permanent record later on. It is never too soon to start indexing a diary, and this adds greatly to its value. Sooner or later, too, you are likely to want to keep notes on animals, birds, or subjects in which you are specially interested in a separate notebook, preferably a loose-leaf one, or even in a card-index. This always sounds very fearsome and scientific, but if your notes are to be of any value to yourself, let alone to other people, there is everything to be said for arranging them in an orderly way.

Photography is a specialized aspect of keeping records that is becoming increasingly popular, but any detailed consideration of its techniques is beyond the scope of this book. For advice on technique, readers are referred to the list at the end of this chapter. Bird photography gets most of the publicity, but birds and mammals are the most difficult British wild animals to photograph because they are so shy. It is usually necessary for the photographer to resort to some sort of concealment, such as a hide. Insects, on the other hand, can be caught and immobilized, while plants are much more amenable, except in a high wind.

Few satisfactory wildlife pictures, except of landscapes or habitats or large birds such as swans on a park lake, can be taken with ordinary cameras and lenses. The most suitable camera for photographing wildlife will depend on whether the photographer wishes to obtain exquisite results from which he can make large exhibition prints or whether he wishes to secure colour transparencies for home projection and for making black-and-white prints suitable for reproduction to illustrate his own field observations.

If the former, the $\frac{1}{4}$-plate format is almost essential. The best type of camera is the field model with ground-glass screen focusing and fitted with a lens of about $8\frac{1}{2}$-inch focal length for birds and mammals or the normal 6-inch lens for habitats, plants, and insects. Such an apparatus means that the photographer will have to get close to his subject and for birds a hiding place will have to be erected near to the nest or bait.

If the latter, then a single-lens 35 mm. reflex camera is the best. Apart from the standard 50 mm. lens, which may be used for habitats, plants, and insects, a number of supplementary lenses should be obtained according to financial resources. For birds and mammals a 135 mm. (or 150 mm.) and a 300 mm. lens will be the most useful, but for 'wait and see' hides or for stalking, a 400 mm. or, better still, a 600 mm. lens will probably give the best results. But an essential when using such long-focus lenses is a heavy, rigid tripod – there is no alternative or substitute to this.

Many people start photographing birds at their nests, because this is the easiest way to find a place on which you can focus a camera with some assurance that a bird will appear in the field of view (Fig. 55). It is most important that newcomers to this aspect of bird photography should learn the all-important unwritten rule that the welfare of the bird and its nest has complete priority over the taking of a satisfactory photograph. A very black mark is awarded to the photographer who by careless or noisy behaviour, or by removing the nest's natural camouflage, causes the bird to desert or a crow to steal the eggs or young.

The Nature Conservancy has taken the lead in building up a National Collection of Nature Photographs, which has been extensively drawn on for the illustrations of this book. The aim is to create a collection of contemporary and historical photographs of the highest standard, suitable for showing at

exhibitions. In the selection of photographs the Conservancy is advised by a committee of photographers under the chairmanship of Eric Hosking.

More and more wildlife photographers are going over to cinematography, and this can be an enthralling pastime. So far, however, remarkably few really first-class films suitable for public exhibition have been made of British wildlife, and those few mainly by a handful of professional teams. A selection of the best-made films of British wildlife in the past few years is given at the end of this chapter.

For watching many forms of wildlife a pair of binoculars is valuable but for birdwatching it is almost indispensable. Even botanists, needing to scrutinize the plants on some lofty cliff or on the other side of a river, find them useful. Excellent advice on the choice and use of binoculars and telescopes for bird watching can be found in the field guide written by J. R. Hebditch for the British Trust for Ornithology. The most important qualities of a pair of prismatic binoculars from the bird watcher's point of view are its magnification and its light-gathering power. These can be calculated from the figures engraved on the instrument itself, e.g. 8 × 40. This means a binocular that magnifies eight times and has an object lens forty millimetres in diameter. The light-gathering power is found by dividing the first of these figures into the second, the result, in the example quoted, being 5. The normally accepted minimum for bird watching is 4, but for watching birds or mammals at night a so-called 'night glass' with a value of 7 is desirable. This is why the British Admiralty specifies 7 × 50 for its binoculars, and many experienced naturalists also go for this specification for their general purpose glass, though 8 and 9 are now the more favoured magnifications among bird watchers. The term 'field glasses', incidentally, though still in general colloquial use for binoculars, strictly applies only to a now outmoded form of non-prismatic instrument.

When choosing a pair of binoculars, it is much better to buy a good second-hand pair, renovated and offered by a reputable firm, than a cheap new pair. Centre eyepiece focusing is preferable to focusing by the separate eyepieces, for this makes it possible to refocus more quickly on a fast-moving animal or bird. For those unfortunate enough to have to wear spectacles out of doors, several special attachments are now marketed, which make it possible to raise the binoculars quickly to the eyes without removing the spectacles. Telescopes are useful for bird watchers specializing in reservoir and estuary watching but are of little use in ordinary country.

An aspect of bird watching that does not call for the use of binoculars, except in the early stages, is finding nests. This is, however, a pastime that is dangerous to the birds, and would-be nest finders should heed the advice of Lord Grey of Fallodon in *The Charm of Birds*:

It is a fascinating pursuit, when there is leisure for it, to look for the nests in the garden or neighbourhood of a country home. The discovery of a well-hidden nest with eggs gives a sense of delicate privilege; the watching of its subsequent welfare is a continuing

56. Badger triplets

interest; and if the end is happy and the young birds leave the nest safely, we feel deeply satisfied. Yet birds, if they could address us, might well say, 'However kindly your interest and however benevolent your intention, please do not look for our nests. You will expose them to dangers of which you do not dream and from which you cannot save them.'

If you do, for instance, in the course of collecting information for the Nest Records Scheme of the British Trust for Ornithology, need to search for nests, then take the greatest care to cover up your tracks afterwards. A trail of footsteps through the long grass or a displaced branch can easily lead to a nest one of the many predators, squirrels, magpies, crows, even grass snakes, that are always on the look-out for a meal of eggs or young birds.

Birds are on the whole much easier to observe than mammals, but for that very reason the pursuit of mammals may exercise an even stronger hold on its devotees than does that of birds. As Ernest Neal, who knows more about badgers (Fig. 56) than anybody else in Britain, has written: 'No naturalist who has once watched badgers is ever content with that one experience. There is something about badger watching that draws you on in spite of cold feet or a series of blank nights.' In badger watching, of course, the first thing is to locate your set, the group of large holes from which the badgers emerge from half an hour to an hour after sunset, according to the time of year and the amount of disturbance to which they are subjected. An occupied set can often be told by the presence of badger hairs adhering to the roots and soil at its entrance. Most sets are among trees or bushes, often on the bank of a stream, and can be told by the large mounds of earth or chalk excavated by the badgers. It is desirable to approach the set at about sunset, against the wind, and to find yourself a perch in good view of the entrance where you will not be too uncomfortable if you have to stay motionless for a long time for fear of frightening the badgers. Fox earths can, of course, be watched in the same way as badger sets, and the playful cubs of both are among the more rewarding sights of British wildlife.

The formation, about ten years ago, of the Deer Group of the Mammal Society has greatly stimulated deer watching as a pastime. Another reason why it has recently become so popular is that our six species of wild deer are not only easily the largest and most conspicuous British land animals, but can also be watched by day, though except in parks and deer forests not without exercising a good deal of patience. The hints on deer watching in the following paragraphs are drawn from the Mammal Society's *Field Guide to British Deer*, which incidentally is much the most comprehensive and helpful field guide to any smaller group of British animals. Much of this advice is also applicable to bird watching.

Deer (Fig. 57) though conspicuous in the open are extremely wary animals, and move off as soon as human beings look like coming within shooting range. So, to start with, it is advisable for the deer watcher himself to wear quiet clothing, olive-green, khaki, or light brown, rather than bright red or blue, in order

to merge as much as possible with the background. The type
of macintosh that rustles should be banished from deer-
watching and indeed from most wildlife expeditions. Field
glasses are essential, for views of deer are often distant, especially in open hilly country; advice here is the same as for
bird watching. When stalking, go against the wind as much as
possible, keeping to cover and not crossing open spaces without looking carefully to see that no deer are in sight. For
watching deer as well as badgers it is a great help to train oneself to stand absolutely still, without even the flicker of an
eyelid, for even this slight movement is enough to alert deer
at close quarters. The ability to freeze to immobility in a split
second is a great help in deer watching. When you do catch sight
of deer, don't move if they have their heads up, and don't try
to get nearer than fifty to eighty yards. Finally, don't disturb
them when you leave (and this applies to bird watching too,
unless you must flush them to prove their identity), or they will
be warier when you return another day to watch again. If you

7. Fallow buck

know your deer ground well enough, you can build a hide near one of their favourite feeding places and watch from there, or climb a tree.

Butterflies, moths, and dragonflies are among the most attractive insects likely to be seen on walks in the country, and each needs to be sought in different places. Well-stocked gardens, country lanes which have not been sprayed with weed-killer, downland and woodland rides are among the best places to see butterflies, and the margins of lakes, ponds, rivers, and streams are the haunt of dragonflies. Moths must either be searched for in their daytime resting places, such as tree trunks and old walls, where they are usually remarkably well camouflaged, or attracted by night with such devices as sugaring and mercury-vapour lamps. Sugaring consists in the smearing on tree-trunks in likely spots of a liquid mixture of brown sugar, treacle, and beer. A mercury-vapour lamp, which emits ultra-violet light, is the most attractive to moths of several types of lamp used by moth collectors. For information on how to collect butterflies, moths, and other insects the reader is referred to the books mentioned at the end of this chapter and Chapter 1, but living insects are far more interesting than those which have been killed. There is still much to learn about the life history of almost every British insect, so a few words on the rearing of caterpillars will not be out of place.

Caterpillars may be obtained either by finding the eggs or caterpillars themselves in the wild or by capturing a female butterfly or moth and inducing her to lay eggs. Comparatively few eggs are large enough to be easily found in the wild; those of the puss moth and some of the hawk-moths are among the exceptions, while other eggs are laid in clumps and may catch the eye. Caterpillars themselves are much more conspicuous, especially some of the woolly bears and other furry ones that are unpalatable to birds and so do not need to conceal themselves. These include the palmer worms, caterpillars of the pure white gold-tail moth, and the handsome drinker caterpillars, so easily seen on the new growing spikes of grass in

April. The woolly bears themselves are the caterpillars of the tiger and ermine moths. Gregarious caterpillars, such as those of the small tortoiseshell butterfly on stinging nettles and the lackey and buff tip moths on various trees, are also easy to find. Caterpillars, of course, should always be fed on the food plant on which they, or the eggs from which they have hatched, were found. This food plant must be kept fresh if picked, and should not be fed to them wet from rain. Ideally the caterpillars should either be kept on a growing plant in a pot, or enclosed in a muslin sleeve on a leafy branch of a growing tree. If kept in a box or other confined space they should not be too crowded, as some caterpillars are liable to turn cannibal. Those moth caterpillars which pupate in the ground should be allowed to do so when the time comes for this stage in their development. Many butterfly caterpillars, on the other hand, will spin up on the side of their cages, or among the twigs of their food plant.

Observing wild flowers is largely a matter of ascertaining the likely places to go to look for them, and going there at the right time of year. The collecting of rarities is not to be encouraged, but a collection of the commoner wild flowers, carefully pressed between sheets of newspaper and mounted afterwards on stiff paper or thin card can give great pleasure. Nowadays, however, many people prefer to collect colour photographs of the wild flowers they see – and this approach is equally applicable to butterflies and moths. Others have taken to colouring in the black-and-white drawings in various books of illustrations of the British flora. Those who colour in the illustrations to the old Bentham and Hooker flora are known by the engaging title of 'Bent-Hooks'. Though this flora itself is outdated, most of the illustrations, by Fitch and Smith, with a later volume of additions by Strudwick to a text by Butcher, are still admirable for this purpose. So are the illustrations in Butcher's new flora, on paper specially chosen for colouring, and in Miss Ross-Craig's still incomplete series.

Almost inevitably the student of freshwater and marine life must collect if he is to see the full range of animals or plants that live in the water. A certain amount can be seen from the bank – whirligig beetles, water skaters, and water-lily and pond-weed leaves on the surface of the pond – and if the water is clear enough, some fish, perhaps minnows or trout or even pike, and various waterweeds swirling in the current. But you must use a net if you want to see more. And here the advice of John Clegg in *The Freshwater Life of the British Isles* should be heeded. If you march noisily to the waterside and splash your net around, you will have little cause to complain if there is nothing there, for you will have frightened everything away. If, on the other hand, you approach the edge of the water cautiously, scrutinize the marginal vegetation carefully for dragonflies and other aquatic insects, and tread lightly as you peer into the water, you will have a better chance of seeing things before you start to catch them. When you start sweeping with your net, do not plunge it at random into the water, but make careful sweeps, first near the surface, then among the water-weeds and finally along the bottom. Thus you will give yourself a chance of sampling each layer of the teeming wildlife of British freshwater streams and ponds. When you get your catches home, do not pour them all into one large aquarium, for some may then eat others, but separate them out into smaller receptacles, such as jam jars or shallow dishes, filled, of course, with pond or rainwater, not with the chlorinated liquid from your household taps.

On the sea shore rather more can be seen without the use of a net, especially at low tide, when many creatures are confined in shallow rock pools. Rocky beaches are best for searching for marine wildlife, for the animals of sandy and muddy shores tend to take refuge under the surface of the sand or mud and so cannot be seen. On rocky shores, however, there is a wide variety of habitats where you can search for marine creatures; even the bare rock surfaces have their limpets and barnacles, while pier and breakwater piles are often living gardens, in which many of the creatures that look like plants are in fact animals.

An increasing number of people are taking to studying the marine life actually under the sea by free and skin diving. Though British waters are never so clear as those of the Mediterranean, much can be seen by the underwater swimmer off our south-western coasts in the summer months. The use of aqualungs, schnorkels, and other underwater swimming equipment is, however, a highly technical and potentially dangerous affair, not to be undertaken without training of some sort.

Under the earth as well as under the sea the modern younger naturalist finds new worlds to explore. Caves give access to the inner secrets of the earth, and the caver or pot-holer spends much of his time in exploring the dark passages of ancient watercourses that honeycomb some of our limestone districts. There is much more to see than just stalactites and stalagmites, beautiful as they are; a fascinating fauna and flora awaits the keen observer. From the moment the cave is entered the changing flora can be observed. The threshold with its flowers and ferns gradually grades away as the light gets dimmer. Here the mosses and lichens dominate the scene and then in turn eventually give way as the last light from the outside vanishes and only a few fungi survive, accompanied on the roof by fungus-gnats (Mycetophilidae). In the pools *Asellus cavaticus*, a relative of the water louse found in streams on the surface, or the blind shrimp *Niphargus* may be searched for. Bats hanging in clusters will give themselves away by a rustling sound as they stir in their fitful sleep. Six species of bat (Fig. 58) shelter in British caves, including the greater and lesser horseshoe bats with their grotesque but highly sensitive faces.

Mountaineering and rock climbing too open up new perspectives for the naturalist. The rock climber, while climbing, has little time to appreciate the wealth around him, though his craft insists he be equipped with a knowledge of the rocks on which he climbs, but when the time comes to rest and eat the hard-earned lunch on some airy perch, then he has the feast of a lifetime. The patterns of the changing scene open up for

133

him, and his companions are the peregrine and the buzzard or *58. Daubenton's* perhaps even the golden eagle or in Snowdonia choughs or *bat* wild goats. He has time to admire the alpine flowers of the rock faces and ledges, the mountain saxifrages, the mountain sorrel, and other gems of these natural rock gardens.

Further Reading

Barrett, John, and Yonge, C.M., *Pocket Guide to the Sea Shore*, 1958.

Campbell, Bruce, *Finding Nests*, 1953.

Cave Research Group, *British Caving*, 1962.

Clegg, John, *The Freshwater Life of the British Isles*, 1952.

Hebditch, J.R., *Binoculars and Telescopes for Field Work*, British Trust for Ornithology Field Guide No. 2, 1961.

Hosking, Eric, and Newberry, Cyril, *Bird Photography as a Hobby*, 1961.

Kenyon, Ley, *Pocket Guide to the Undersea World*, 1956.

Newman, L.Hugh, *Looking at Butterflies*, 1959.

Page, F. J. Taylor, *Field Guide to British Deer*, Mammal Society Field Guide No. 1, 1959.
Stokoe, W. J., *The Caterpillars of the British Butterflies*, 1944.
Warham, John, *The Technique of Bird Photography*, 1956.

Some Good Films of British Wildlife

Between the Tides, British Transport Film Library, 1958.
Garden Birds, Royal Society for the Protection of Birds, 1962.
Highland Birds, R.S.P.B., 1958.
Island of Birds, R.S.P.B., 1959.
Journey into Spring, B.T.F.L., 1957.
The Life History of the Alder Woodwasp and its Insect Enemies, Council for Nature, 1960.
The Marsh Fritillary Butterfly, Gaumont-British Film Library, 1961.
Reserved for Birds, R.S.P.B., 1961.
The Rival World, Petroleum Films Bureau, 1955.
River of Life, G.B.F.L., 1961.
Sea-bird Summer, R.S.P.B., 1960.
Wild Highlands, B.T.F.L., 1962.

8 Conservation in Britain

The new modern approach to nature conservation in Britain is still hardly understood by the general public. Hitherto the accent has been on preservation, a kind of embalming of the countryside in a museum atmosphere and a desperate struggle to save certain animal and plant species from extinction. Conservation, on the other hand, is a positive concept: the management of land so as to maintain and increase the natural resources, soil, water, timber, grasses, other vegetation, and animals, for use and not necessarily by cultivation.

In its beginnings, however, the conservation movement was all preservation and protection. Right back in the Middle Ages primitive attempts, such as the forest laws of the Norman kings, were made to preserve game animals, and these, continuing into the modern age of efficient guns, have wrought far-reaching and often catastrophic changes in the populations of our predatory animals. Foxes, polecats, hawks, and owls have been controlled and frequently killed off because they were thought to be harmful to the interests of the game, notwithstanding that both the predators and their prey had coexisted happily for thousands of years before man thought of 'protecting' the game. The consequences of game preservation for the other wildlife of Britain have never been properly studied, but there can be little doubt that among them is the vast proliferation of pests in the countryside, pests that should have been controlled by the missing predators.

The first man in Britain to try to protect birds other than game birds was the eccentric nineteenth-century Yorkshire landowner Charles Waterton: this was indeed one of his eccentricities in the eyes of his neighbours, and of his scandalized gamekeeper who was forbidden to shoot owls. Waterton too was probably the first man to put up nestboxes purely to attract birds for the pleasure of seeing them. Not till the mid century did more orthodox ornithologists come round to the idea of bird protection, and this began formally in Britain with the passing of an Act of Parliament to protect seabirds in 1869. At this time one of the favourite 'sports' was to go out in a boat and take pot shots at gulls and other seabirds; and, if you visited a breeding colony, of course it was even greater 'fun', for you had a much better chance of killing the birds as they agitatedly milled around their nests. One of the hazards that gulls had to face when they first began to come up the Thames to Central London before the Embankment was built was people shooting at them from the bridges.

In 1880 the first fairly comprehensive Act to protect wild birds was passed, and this was followed nine years later by the foundation of the (now Royal) Society for the Protection of Birds, under the Presidency of the Duchess of Portland, who continued in this office till her death sixty-five years later. Piecemeal bird protection legislation continued over the years till it was tidied up and made more comprehensive in the Protection of Birds Act 1954. The only other law protecting specific non-game animals is the Grey Seals Protection Act of 1912. County councils, however, have the power to make by-laws prohibiting the uprooting of wild plants on land to which the public have access, and all but a handful of the English and half the Welsh county councils have in fact made such bylaws.

The R.S.P.B. soon began to create bird sanctuaries and appoint wardens to guard the nesting sites of the rarer birds, such as peregrine falcons and red-necked phalaropes, on land which it did not own or lease. It was not until 1912, however, that naturalists generally, spurred by the Hon. Charles Rothschild, came together to found the Society for the Promotion of Nature Reserves, which he handsomely endowed. The nascent nature-protection movement was dealt a heavy blow by the First World War, and there was little constructive achievement by any of the bodies concerned between the wars. The

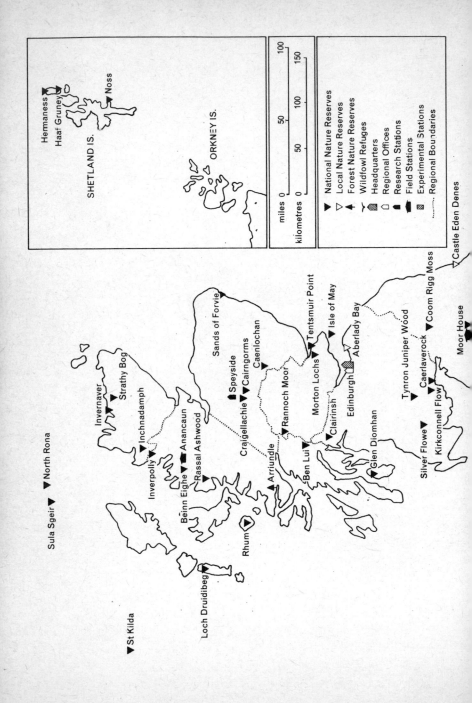

SHETLAND IS.

Hermaness
Haaf Gruney
Noss

ORKNEY IS.

miles 0   50   100

kilometres 0   50   100   150

▼ National Nature Reserves
▽ Local Nature Reserves
◄ Forest Nature Reserves
▶◖▨ Wildfowl Refuges
◖ Headquarters
◐ Regional Offices
◖ Research Stations
▨ Field Stations
▨ Experimental Stations
····· Regional Boundaries

Sula Sgeir ▼   ▼ North Rona

▼ St Kilda

Loch Druidibeg ◀

Rhum ⬡

Inverpolly ▼
Bèinn Eighe ▼
Rassal Ashwood
Anancaun ▲
Arriundle ◀

Invernaver ▼
Strathy Bog ▼
Inchnadamph ▼

Sands of Forvie ▼

Speyside ▪
Craigellachie ▼
Cairngorms
Caenlochan

Rannoch Moor ▼
Ben Lui ▲
Clairinsh ▼
Morton Lochs ▼

Tentsmuir Point ▼
Isle of May ▼
Aberlady Bay ▽
Edinburgh ◖▨

Glen Diomhan ▼

Tynron Juniper Wood ▼
Caerlaverock ▼
Silver Flowe ▼
Kirkconnell Flow ▼
Coom Rigg Moss ▼

Moor House ▼

Castle Eden Denes ▽

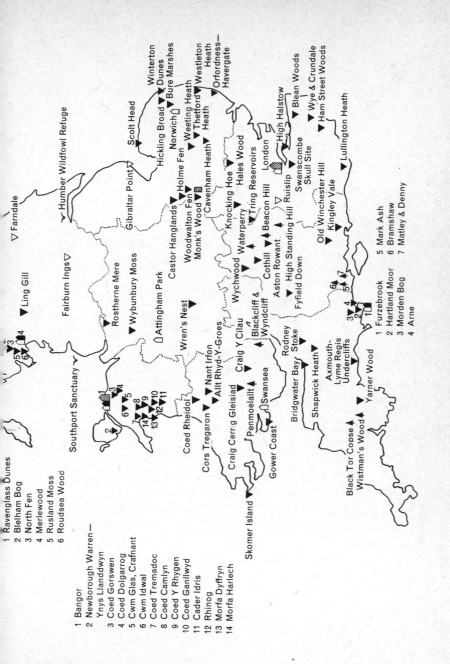

1 Ravenglass Dunes
2 Bielham Bog
3 North Fen
4 Merlewood
5 Rusland Moss
6 Roudsea Wood

1 Bangor
2 Newborough Warren —
  Ynys Llanddwyn
3 Coed Gorswen
4 Coed Dolgarrog
5 Cwm Glas, Crafnant
6 Cwm Idwal
7 Coed Tremadoc
8 Coed Camlyn
9 Coed Y Rhygen
10 Coed Ganllwyd
11 Cader Idris
12 Rhinog
13 Morfa Dyffryn
14 Morfa Harlech

1 Furzebrook
2 Hartland Moor
3 Morden Bog
4 Arne

5 Mark Ash
6 Bramshaw
7 Matley & Denny

▽ Farndale

↙ Humber Wildfowl Refuge

Winterton
Dunes
Hickling Broad ▶ ▶ Bure Marshes
Holme Fen ▶ Weeting Heath ▶ Westleton
Norwich ◻ ▶ Thetford ▶ Heath
Woodwalton Fen ▶ Heath ▶ Orfordness—
Monk's Wood ◩ ▶ Havergate
Cavenham Heath ▶

Scolt Head ◁

Blean Woods ▶
Wye & Crundale ▶
Ham Street Woods ▶
▶ Lullington Heath

High Halstow ▶
London ◻
Swanscombe
Skull Site ◩
Old Winchester Hill ▶
Kingley Vale ▶

Gibraltar Point ◁

Fairburn Ings ▽

Rostherne Mere ▶

Wybunbury Moss ▶

Castor Hanglands ▶
Knocking Hoe ▶
Hales Wood ▶
Waterperry ▶
Tring Reservoirs ▶

Wychwood ▶
Cothill ▶
Beacon Hill ▶
Aston Rowant ▶
High Standing Hill ▽
Fyfield Down ▶

Attingham Park ◻

Wren's Nest ▶

Nant Irfon ▶
Allt Rhyd-Y-Groes ▶

Craig Y Cilau ▶
Blackcliff & ▶
Wyndcliff ▶
Rodney ◀
Stoke

Coed Rheidol ▶

Cors Tregaron ▶

Craig Cerrig Gleisiad ▶

Penmoelallt ▶

Southport Sanctuary ↙

Swansea ◻
Gower Coast ◻

Bridgwater Bay ◀
Shapwick Heath ▶

Axmouth-
Lyme Regis ▶
Undercliffs
Yarner Wood ▶

Black Tor Copse ▲
Wistman's Wood ▲

Skomer Island ▶

▶ Ling Gill

3 4 5
6 ◄

6 ▶
3 4 5 ◀ 7
3 4 1
2

Second World War, however, gave the whole movement a much needed fillip. The S.P.N.R. promoted a Nature Reserves Investigation Committee, which prepared a list of proposed national nature reserves and conservation areas, based on the pioneer list produced by Rothschild in 1915. At the same time the British Ecological Society drew up a blueprint for what eventually became the Nature Conservancy, a national official body concerned with the conservation of wildlife, soundly based on field research. The reconstruction fervour that marked the period 1943-6 enabled a Wildlife Special Conservation Committee, under the chairmanship of Dr (now Sir) Julian Huxley, to be appointed under the aegis of the Ministry of Town and Country Planning's National Parks Committee. The Huxley Committee married the reports of the N.R.I.C. and the B.E.S., and on the basis of its Report,* made in 1947, the Nature Conservancy was set up under Royal Charter in 1949, and became a research council parallel to the Agricultural and Medical Research Councils.

Since the war the final bricks have been laid on the arch of British nature conservation with the appearance, especially since 1956, of a chain of county naturalists' trusts, which now cover the whole of England and Wales, and the creation in 1958 of the Council for Nature, to act as an unofficial mouthpiece of the natural history movement in conservation matters requiring national action.

The functions of the Nature Conservancy, as set out in its charter are as follows: 'to provide scientific advice on the conservation and control of the natural flora and fauna of Great Britain; to establish, maintain, and manage nature reserves in Great Britain, including the maintenance of physical features of scientific interest; and to organize and develop the research services related thereto'. The research functions of the Conservancy were briefly discussed in Chapter 5. Its conservation functions have so far been mainly concerned with the creation of ninety-five national nature reserves, with a total acreage of

* *Conservation of Nature in England and Wales*, Cmd 7122.

186,992, the great bulk of which is in Scotland (Fig. 59). More than one-third of the total acreage is owned by the Conservancy, more than half is held by agreement with the landowners, and the balance leased.

Some of the most famous natural history sites in Britain are now safeguarded by the Conservancy in its reserves (Figs. 60 to 62). They include part of Glen Clova in the eastern Highlands, Tregaron Bog in Cardiganshire, Cwm Idwal in Snowdonia, Hickling Broad and Scolt Head Island in Norfolk, Noss in the Shetlands, St Kilda beyond the Outer Hebrides, and the site where the Swanscombe skull was found in North Kent in 1935–6. The Cairngorms reserve, at nearly 40,000 acres, is one of the largest nature reserves in Europe; two more Scottish reserves, Inverpolly and Rhum, contain over 26,000 acres each; and the largest English reserve is Moor House in the Pennines, with 10,000 acres. Others are much smaller, down to a few acres. The Conservancy has aimed to build up a representative sample of natural habitats throughout Great Britain, and now has a

60. National ature Reserve: Lullington Heath, Sussex

1. National
Nature Reserve:
Beinn Eighe,
Wester Ross

wide range of woodlands, bogs and mosses, sand dunes, down-land, and marine islands. Habitats of this kind are otherwise in great danger of destruction; bogs and marshes, for instance, from being drained, deciduous woodlands from being felled and replaced by conifers, chalk grassland on the downs from becoming overgrown with hawthorn and other scrub. It is part of the Conservancy's task to carry out research to find the best methods of averting such preventable dangers as erosion and loss of plant nutrients due to moor-burning and over-grazing, and 'bushing up' of heaths and chalk and limestone grasslands. For each of its reserves the Conservancy prepares a management plan.

In addition to the national nature reserves there are eleven forest nature reserves, maintained by agreement with the Forestry Commission and other official bodies; two wildfowl refuges, at Southport in Lancashire and on the Humber; and seven local nature reserves, declared by local authorities on

2. National
Nature Reserve:
Cader Idris,
Merioneth

the advice of the Conservancy. These latter include such well-known sites as the gullery and ternery at Ravenglass in Cumberland, Aberlady Bay in the Firth of Forth, the famous wild daffodil site at Farndale in the North Riding of Yorkshire (Fig. 63), and the sand dunes and bird migration station at Gibraltar Point on the Lincolnshire corner of the Wash.

Much of the Conservancy's time is taken up in fending off threats to important natural history sites all over Great Britain from building and other development, on which the Conservancy must be consulted under existing legislation, and from agriculture, forestry, and drainage, which must be averted by persuasion and negotiation. The main instrument used by the Conservancy in this aspect of its work is the scheduling of large numbers of Sites of Special Scientific Interest all over the country. These are sites not warranting acquisition as national nature reserves, which it is nevertheless desirable to save as potential local reserves. Once scheduled by the Conservancy, they are notified to the local planning authorities, who must warn the Conservancy of any proposed development affecting

63. Local
Nature Reserve
Farndale, York

them. In extreme cases, such as Dungeness, the shingle foreland in Kent where the conservation movement lost, and Berry Head, the limestone headland in South Devon, where it won, the issue has to be pressed to a public inquiry, but often dangers can be averted by negotiation before this stage.

The Conservancy also provides a scientific advisory service on problems of the conservation and control of wildlife, for, looked at properly, conservation and control are two aspects of the same thing, since an animal or plant only needs to be controlled when its conservation has got out of hand. Among the problems in this field on which it is advising at the time of writing are water conservation, a question which has been raised in an acute form by Manchester Corporation's recently frustrated designs on Ullswater and other sources of water in the Lake District; the use of poisonous chemicals in agriculture, and especially the dressing of seed corn with certain substances highly poisonous to mammals and birds; the spraying of roadside and railway verges with weedkiller; the preservation of the coastline; fires in woodland and on heaths and moors; the pollution of the sea by oil; and the control of various mammals, including red deer, grey seals, coypus, rabbits, and grey squirrels.

The Nature Conservancy has two counterparts in the voluntary sphere: for its advisory functions and threats to sites the Council for Nature, and for its nature-reserve functions the Society for the Promotion of Nature Reserves. In fact, the Council for Nature usually joins with the Conservancy in opposing the development of S.S.S.I.s, such as Berry Head and the Chiltern escarpment beechwood where the Post Office recently attempted to erect a 250-foot tower. The Council, however, is freer to act where a site is regarded as important by local naturalists but has not yet been registered as an S.S.S.I. For instance, when it was proposed to site a sewage farm close to Selborne village in Hampshire, a Mecca for naturalists from all over the English-speaking world because it was Gilbert White's home, the Council for Nature was better placed to make a successful protest than the Conservancy. The Council's Conservation Committee is also concerned with such national problems as the control of the grey seal and of wild deer in England and Wales.

The Society for the Promotion of Nature Reserves was founded, as its name suggests, to acquire, or promote the acquisition of, nature reserves in Great Britain. At the time of writing it possesses or leases nine reserves, all in England, and has grant-aided the acquisition by other bodies of half a dozen others. The Society's most important reserve is Woodwalton Fen in Huntingdonshire, now leased to the Nature Conservancy as a national nature reserve. Smaller reserves are in Buckinghamshire, Westmorland, Somerset, Gloucestershire, Cheshire, Suffolk, and Wiltshire, and include one of the very few known sites in Britain for a rare buttercup, and a fine example of a fritillary meadow at Mickfield, Suffolk. Among the important reserves grant-aided by the Society are Scotton and Linwood Commons in Lincolnshire, Steep Holm in the Bristol Channel, the only site in the British Isles for the wild peony, and the

Calf of Man. In recent years the S.P.N.R. has both acted as midwife at the birth of the Council for Nature, making it grants of £2,500 to cover initial administrative costs, and provided an umbrella for the growing county naturalists' trusts movement.

The National Trust has many important nature reserves among its numerous properties. They include Wicken Fen in Cambridgeshire, Blakeney Point and Scolt Head Island in Norfolk, and the Farne Islands off the coast of Northumberland. The Trust's advisory committee on nature reserves was abolished a few years ago, but has now been revived and this should enable the National Trust to play a more active part in the nature conservation movement than it has done in the past few years.

Until five or six years ago, the nature conservation movement in Britain was almost entirely on a national basis, run from London and out of touch with much of the local knowledge that might have warned when important sites were in danger. This has been largely remedied by the creation of a chain of county naturalists' trusts that has run like wildfire across England and Wales during the past five years. This movement began in Norfolk in 1926, when Dr Sidney Long and a group of friends had the foresight to realize that this was the best way of saving important natural history sites in the English county which is richest in them. For one important difference between a naturalists' trust and a natural history society is that the trust is registered as a company limited by guarantee and so can own and lease land, while a society, being unincorporated, cannot. Those few societies which do have nature reserves or bird sanctuaries have to appoint special trustees to hold the land. In fact the whole purpose and structure of a trust, with its emphasis on conservation, is different from that of a natural history society with its emphasis on research and observation, and trusts do attract support from many people who do not regard themselves as naturalists.

When the Norfolk Naturalists' Trust was founded, the hope

was expressed at the meeting of the British Association in 1926 that every county would soon follow suit, but in fact for twenty years Norfolk was left to plough a lonely furrow. It put this time to good use, and now owns or leases no fewer than twenty-five reserves in its county, far more than any other trust. Among them are such famous sites as Scolt Head, Cley Marshes, Wretham Heath and Whiteslea estate at Hickling. As many as seven of the sites carefully husbanded over the years by the Norfolk Trust are now included in national nature reserves.

Yorkshire was the second county to launch a trust, in 1946, and now has three reserves, two of them, Askham Bog near York and Spurn Head at the mouth of the Humber, of first-class importance. Lincolnshire came third, in 1948, and with its dozen reserves scattered throughout one of the most heavily cultivated counties in Britain, can fairly claim to be the most active of the post-war trusts. At Gibraltar Point, on the corner of the Wash, this Trust both manages a reserve of some 1,300 acres for Lindsey County Council and Skegness Urban District Council and maintains a field research station which is also an important link in the national chain of bird observatories. In 1956 trusts were founded both for Leicestershire and for Cambridgeshire with the Isle of Ely, followed in 1957 by the West Midlands (Staffordshire, Warwickshire, and Worcestershire), and in 1958 by Kent. The next year saw the beginning of the tidal flow of trust formation, with two more trusts, one for Surrey and one for Berkshire, Buckinghamshire, and Oxfordshire; in 1960 Essex, Bedfordshire with Huntingdonshire, and Hampshire with the Isle of Wight started up. A vintage year was 1961 with seven new trusts founded (Devon, Derbyshire, Dorset, Glamorgan, Gloucestershire, Suffolk, Sussex) and the old-established West Wales Field Society, which had been running its reserves through trustees, converting itself into a trust. At the time of writing in the autumn of 1962 trusts have also started in Cheshire, Cornwall, Durham with Northumberland, Herefordshire with Radnorshire, the Lake District,

Lancashire, Shropshire, and Wiltshire, while the process of formation has begun in Hertfordshire with Middlesex. Discussions about the formation of trusts are also in progress in Monmouthshire, Northamptonshire, Nottinghamshire, Perthshire, and Somerset. The trusts are all represented on the County Naturalists' Trusts Committee of the Society for the Promotion of Nature Reserves which provides them with a focusing point in much the same way that the British Trust for Ornithology does for the bird observatories.

Those who have had the experience of founding and running a county naturalists' trust know that as soon as it appears on the scene innumerable problems are dumped in its lap. Besides their main *raison d'être*, the creation of nature reserves and bird sanctuaries by acquisition, lease or agreement, there are many other ways in which wildlife can be conserved. Some of the practical problems, such as removal of scrub and other unwanted vegetation, are discussed in the next chapter, but a glance at the recent achievements of some of the trusts will show how very varied are the calls on the time and limited resources of their almost entirely voluntary personnel. Several trusts have negotiated successfully with their county surveyors to spare from spraying or other disturbance rare and attractive wild flowers on road verges. Cambridgeshire and the Isle of Ely has specialized in the saving of parish pits and ponds, most important reservoirs of wildlife in a highly agricultural county, by agreement with parish councils. Hampshire and the Isle of Wight has erected nestboxes in the New Forest to encourage redstarts and other hole-nesting birds. Berks, Bucks, and Oxon saved a heronry from destruction by intervening when the wood was being felled; other trusts have asked their county councils to put tree preservation orders on heronry trees. Devon is investigating the damage done by commercial primrose picking. Leicestershire has arranged for little-used sections of the canals in its county to be preserved as nature reserves. Lincolnshire has virtually completed its survey of sites suitable for preservation in the county.

All the bodies so far discussed are concerned with the conservation of wildlife and nature in the broadest sense, but there are also a number of others which cover particular groups only, and of these by far the most important is the Royal Society for the Protection of Birds, which has in the past few years more than doubled its membership, now standing at over 15,000. The Society has more than a score of bird sanctuaries in various parts of Great Britain, some of them of the highest importance, such as its two Suffolk coastal reserves, Havergate Island the only breeding place in Britain of the avocet, and Minsmere Level, now almost the only breeding place of the marsh harrier. Northward Hill on the north coast of Kent, with its important heronry, is another sanctuary owned by the Society which has been declared a national nature reserve. At Dungeness, where the Society has long held an area of the shingle which was formerly a breeding place for the Kentish plover and still has a number of interesting and uncommon breeding birds, it maintains a warden under grant from the Central Electricity Generating Board, to ensure that no harm is done to the wildlife of the area outside that on which the nuclear power station is being built. In Scotland the Society has recently, by arrangement with the landowners, declared a number of sanctuaries on islands in the Firths of Forth and Clyde, which are the sites of important terneries. Steps have had to be taken to exterminate the rats which were endangering the existence of some of these colonies.

To the credit of the R.S.P.B. stands the restoration as British breeding birds of three or four species lost during the nineteenth and early twentieth centuries. For sixteen years the breeding colony of the avocet has been safeguarded on Havergate Island, often at considerable cost, as when the sea-walls of this island in the estuary of the River Ore were broken down by the tidal surge of 31 January 1953. The black-tailed godwit had also been carefully guarded at its still secret breeding site 'somewhere in England'; at least a dozen pairs have now bred there annually for some years past. Both these wading birds were lost during the first half of the last century, largely due to drainage of their breeding haunts in eastern England. The osprey or fish hawk, which hung on longer, till the reign of King Edward VII, has been the latest to return. A single pair has now bred or attempted to breed for nearly ten years in the Loch Garten area of Strathspey, and for the past five years has been the most carefully guarded pair of wild birds in British history. Following a catastrophe in 1958, when a kleptomaniac egg collector robbed the nest under the eyes of the watchers, smashing the eggs in his flight, a day and night watch has been kept during the breeding season, and in each year since then two or three young have been successfully reared. The public are invited to view the nest from a hide through powerful binoculars, and as a result between 15,000 and 20,000 people have seen the ospreys each year. A fourth bird which the Society can now claim the credit for preserving as British is the marsh harrier, for since the breeding pairs disappeared from Norfolk in 1960 the R.S.P.B. reserve at Minsmere has been the British headquarters of this fine bird of prey.

The R.S.P.B. has many other activities. Its journal *Bird Notes* is one of the liveliest natural history journals published in Britain. It has joined with the British Trust for Ornithology to collect evidence on the killing of birds by poisonous farm chemicals, and has succeeded in proving its case and forcing the Government to ban the use of aldrin, dieldrin, and heptachlor on seed-dressings at certain times of year. It has always been interested in the problem of birds killed at lighthouses, and now maintains floodlighting equipment at five lighthouses which by lighting up the towers has greatly diminished deaths at some of them. It has recently appointed an Education Officer, and now runs courses for bird watchers at its new country headquarters in Bedfordshire. Its Junior Bird Recorders' Club has already been mentioned.

Conservation of wild ducks, geese, and swans, both at home and abroad, is the special province of the Wildfowl Trust, which achieves its aims partly through its superb collections of wildfowl at Slimbridge, Gloucestershire, and Peakirk, North-amptonshire, and partly through its research unit, which studies both wild populations in the field and the diseases of wildfowl in the collections. Through the good offices of the Nature Conservancy the Trust participates with the wildfowlers in a special committee on wildfowl conservation. Among other things, this advises the Conservancy on the national wildfowl refuges, of which two have already been set up, at Southport, Lancashire, and on the Humber. The Wildfowlers' Association of Great Britain and Ireland also has its own extensive pro-gramme of wildfowl conservation, involving reserves and re-fuges all over the country.

The Botanical Society of the British Isles is concerned with the conservation of plant life. Though much of its former attention to individual sites is now funnelled off on to the county naturalists' trusts, there are still many problems await-ing consideration, such as excessive picking of wild flowers, enforcement of county bylaws against uprooting, the com-mercial collection of moss from downland and sphagnum bogs, the effect of roadside spraying, and the creation of machinery whereby the sites of extremely rare plants can be safeguarded without giving away the locality. When important sites are threatened, the B.S.B.I. prepares evidence on their botanical value for submission to public inquiries or submits protests to the organizations concerned. The Society's Conservation Committee has regular meetings with the Nature Conservancy to consider these problems, and there are parallel meetings on entomological conservation problems between the Conservancy and the Royal Entomological Society.

Protection of British mammals is the concern of the Fauna Preservation Society and the Universities' Federation for Animal Welfare. This brings us to the verge of international nature protection, which, though strictly beyond the scope of this book, may be briefly mentioned. The primary concern of the Fauna Preservation Society is to save the larger mammals of the world, and especially of Africa. British interest in protecting rare birds in other parts of the world is looked after by the British Section of the International Council for Bird Preservation, whose constituent members are the R.S.P.B. and seven other leading societies concerned with bird protection, with five other societies as associate members. It was the British Section which was recently responsible for choosing the robin as Britain's national bird. One of its major recent achievements was to persuade the Royal Air Force to desist from practice-bombing the sandbanks at the mouth of the Elbe each year at the time when the major part of the shelduck population of north-western Europe, including the British Isles, is moulting there and in a flightless condition.

Newest comer of all on the international scene is the World Wildlife Fund, which was set up in the autumn of 1961 to raise funds on a massive scale to help save the fast-vanishing wildlife of many parts of the world. Some £50,000 had already been raised by the Fund in Britain before the spring of 1962, when a separate, but linked, British National Appeal was launched. This is only in its very early days at the time of writing, but already more than £70,000 has been subscribed. Of the sums raised by the British appeal, approximately one-third will go to the international fund in Zürich, another third will be retained in Britain for conservation at home, and the balance will be available either at home or abroad, wherever the need is greatest.

Further Reading

Brown, P.E., and Waterston, George, *The Return of the Osprey*, 1962.

Nicholson, E.M., *Britain's Nature Reserves*, 1957.

Annual Reports of the Nature Conservancy and other bodies mentioned.

9 How to Help Conserve Wildlife

It is not enough for the naturalist or country lover merely to subscribe to some organization and then think he or she has discharged his duty. If the wildlife of Britain is to be saved for future generations to enjoy, naturalists and country lovers must themselves be prepared to do something to help, in addition to subscribing to the essential task of keeping the organizing bodies going.

The individual walker in the countryside, for instance, has a responsibility not only for observing the Country Code himself, but for rectifying the consequences of breaches of it by others: not only to shut gates himself but to shut those left open by others; not only to refrain from lighting fires, but to put out those carelessly started by others; not only to take his own litter home, but to ask others politely to do the same, if he sees them throwing it down. Those in charge of parties of sight-seeing naturalists bear a special responsibility to ensure that their group does not disturb birds from their nests or trample down rare plants. More than one of the last dozen pairs of the kite in mid Wales has been made to desert its nest in recent years by people picnicking too near the tree.

Every year rare orchids are picked by people who have no idea of their rarity, so that it is advisable to confine casual flower-picking for pleasure to well-known or plainly abundant wild flowers. Even then, it is better to leave the flowers for others to enjoy. It is also quite unjustifiable to uproot rare plants for your garden. Nor is it as well known as it should be that in all but four English counties it is an offence under county bylaws to uproot a wild plant in a public place. If you should see an offence under one of these bylaws being committed, you should take similar action to that described below for infractions of the bird protection laws, and afterwards notify either the Council for Nature or the Botanical Society of the British Isles.

Another aspect of practical wildlife conservation is the enforcement of the Protection of Birds Act, for there can never be enough police to catch all offenders and it must often happen that the only witness to an offence is a private citizen. The Royal Society for the Protection of Birds issues a useful free leaflet on how bird lovers and other members of the public can help in enforcing the law. The first thing, of course, is to familiarize oneself with the actual terms of the Act. With certain exceptions all wild birds and their eggs are protected, while some rarer birds are protected by special penalties. The maximum penalties for each bird, egg, or nest are £5 for the commoner ones and £25 for the rarer ones, with up to a month's imprisonment. There are certain birds on a black list; these may be killed or have their eggs taken by authorized persons (this is most important, for most casual shooters will not have obtained permission from a landowner to shoot on his land). These include the cormorant, carrion and hooded crows, feral pigeon, herring and black-backed gulls, jackdaw, jay, magpie, rook, shag, house sparrow, starling, stock dove, and woodpigeon; in certain fruit-growing districts the bullfinch; and, in Scotland only, the goosander, red-breasted merganser, and rock dove. They are all harmful, or believed to be so, to agriculture, fisheries, or game preservation. Some more exceptions should also be borne in mind. It is quite legal to take a wild bird for the purpose of ringing it and releasing it again; to take an injured bird in order to care for it and release it again when it has recovered; and to kill a seriously injured or sick bird. In the last two cases, the bird must not have been injured by the rescuer's own act.

With this background information in mind, the R.S.P.B. advises people, who witness an offence being committed, first to try to stop the nest being robbed or the bird being caught or killed. In these circumstances, it is usually impracticable to summon the police, though this of course is ideally desirable, for the offender must give his name and address to a policeman, but need not do so to a private citizen. If you are alone and the offender refuses you his name and address, memorize his appearance, make a note of his car number if any, and if possible follow him till either you meet a policeman or he enters a house. You must, of course, be quite sure that you have seen him actually committing an offence and not just acting in a suspicious manner. Any witness besides yourself will be very valuable. Armed with as much detailed information as you can muster, written down as soon after the event as possible, you can then go to the police. After this, the R.S.P.B. would also be very glad to hear about the incident, in case they are able to offer specialist advice.

A more positive approach, for those who, like Dr Bruce Campbell in Oxfordshire and Mr K. G. Spencer in Lancashire, have the gift for working with young people, is to try to canalize the interest of young bird-nesters and shooters into bird watching and bird study. Even an offer to talk to the local youth club may achieve something, and the Boy Scouts in your district will no doubt welcome a talk to explain the background of their rule that Scouts may not collect birds' eggs.

One step that almost every reader of this book must surely be in a position to take is to join his local county naturalists' trust (see list in Appendix) and offer to help in its affairs. Trusts welcome all kinds of help from envelope-addressing to wardening of rare birds and plants or talks to women's institutes and other local bodies on their work. Many people, such as journalists, printers, solicitors, teachers, farmers, and land agents have specialized knowledge that will be most valuable to a trust. Teachers in particular can do a great deal by using the reserves of their local trust for practical demonstrations of how wildlife lives and what their children can do to help to conserve it.

For younger and more energetic conservationists a new method of helping personally in the tasks of conservation has recently become possible through the Conservation Corps, which was pioneered by the Council for Nature and has been taken up all over the country by the naturalists' trusts (Figs. 64 and 65). At one time it was thought that all that was necessary to maintain a nature reserve was to put a fence round it and not let anybody in. Now, thanks to two generations of work by the ecologists, it is generally realized that nature is far from static, and that to put a fence round a reserve and do nothing else is merely to invite the destruction of the habitat by natural forces: many of our most familiar habitats, such as chalk or limestone grassland, fen, and coppiced woodland are in fact highly unstable and often kept in being only by human intervention, such as grazing by cattle or sheep for the grassland, or sedge-cutting for the fens. The major problem in reserve maintenance in recent years has been the consequences of the widespread cessation of sheep grazing on the downs, which meant the bushing up of huge areas of downland, especially since the myxomatosis epidemic of 1954–6 also reduced the grazing pressure from rabbits. Thus large areas of open

64. The Conservation Corps at work: clearing out a pond on Chorleywood Common, Herts.

5. The Conservation Corps at work: planting marram grass at Newborough Warren, Anglesey

country, which were given to bodies such as the National Trust in the belief that this would preserve them as open walking country for ever, have in fact become grown over with hawthorn, dogwood, and other scrub. The problem has become an acute one, and if any open downland at all is to be preserved for future generations, a substantial amount of labour must be forthcoming for the eradication and control of the scrub.

It is not surprising therefore that scrub control has been the major task of the Conservation Corps since its first field day on Box Hill in the North Downs of Surrey in February 1959. The Corps was originally set up with the aid of a generous grant of £3,000 a year for three years from the Carnegie United Kingdom Trust, which later extended its aid for a further two years. Its aim from the start has been to enable young people to serve the community in educational tasks which help to preserve the countryside and its wild life and at the same time to give them an enjoyable 'hard-work holiday'. An important aspect of the Corps' work is the talks given by naturalists to its members in the evenings, when the reasons for the work they are doing in the daytime are explained to them. At first most of the tasks were residential ones for a week or a fortnight, but, following a favourable mention in the Albemarle Report on youth work, the Ministry of Education made the Council a grant of £3,000 a year to enable the Corps to expand and cover week-end tasks, drawing in boys from clubs and other youth organizations.

The Corps' work during its first four years has consisted, in addition to scrub clearance, of such maintenance tasks as the clearing of overgrown and silted-up ponds and watercourses, eradication of unwanted cord-grass *Spartina townsendii* from saltmarshes, tree-planting and planting of marram grass on sand dunes. Most of the Corps' tasks have been in such famous nature reserves as Wicken and Woodwalton Fens, Box Hill, and Gibraltar Point, but many have also been in less well-known places, often belonging to county naturalists' trusts, from the south of England to the north of Scotland. At present about five hundred different volunteers take part in the work each year. Membership of the Corps is open to any able-bodied person aged sixteen or over, who should apply to its Organizer, Brigadier E. F. E. Armstrong, at the Council for Nature. Volunteers are expected to pay a small contribution towards their keep, and, except on week-end tasks, part of their fares.

The National Trust for Scotland also runs work parties of this sort, especially on St Kilda, and more recently the county naturalists' trusts have started organizing conservation corps of their own. Such corps are already at work in Buckinghamshire, Cambridgeshire, Gloucestershire, Kent, Leicestershire, and Lincolnshire, among others. One of the tasks undertaken has been the clearing of scrub from Darwin's famous orchid bank at Downe, Kent, where the great naturalist made many of his observations on wild orchids.

The practical conservation of wildlife can start in the back garden by feeding the birds and putting up nestboxes for them to breed in. Even before that, judicious planting in the garden will provide the birds with food and, incidentally, often divert them from fruit and vegetables that you would prefer not to share with them. So plant plenty of berry-bearing trees and shrubs in your garden, cotoneasters, rowans, pyracanthas, cherries, hollies, and hawthorns for the thrushes. Bushes in the garden also provide useful cover for the birds. And don't forget some ordinary annual sunflowers for the finches, especially the greenfinches. If you can bear to, leave some seeding thistles or other weeds in a corner; the birds will bless you even if your neighbours do not.

When the ground is hard with frost, or even when it is not, it is a great help to insect-eaters such as robins and thrushes to fork over a small patch of bare soil to stir up the earthworms and other soil invertebrates. Your garden robin will come and wait upon you when he sees you digging and will fly down to feed as soon as you have gone.

But during the winter many of these natural sources of food will give out and unless you feed the birds they will either leave your garden to search for food elsewhere or die of starvation. In northern countries many birds only survive through the winter because they are fed by kindly people. This certainly happens, for instance, with the great tit in northern Sweden, and is probably true to a large extent of both great and blue tits, as well as other birds, in Britain in a hard winter. Busy people may find some of the specially made-up bird foods that are marketed nowadays a time-saver, but there are plenty of everyday foods that cost little or nothing. Foods that appeal to a great many birds include shredded suet, wholemeal bread, porridge and coarse oats, and small lumps of cheese. If you are prepared to go to the trouble of cooking food especially for the birds, you can offer them boiled rice mixed with melted fat, pressure-cooked fish scraps and bones, potatoes baked in their jackets and chopped up and mixed with coarse oats, oatmeal, or fat, and stale bread or cake crumbs mixed with fat and a few currants. Tits like cheese, fats (old cooking fat will do), bacon and ham rinds, and nuts. You can also give them a fresh coconut cut in half but not on any account dried shredded coconut which will swell in their stomachs and kill them. Blackbirds, thrushes, and starlings love rotten apples but it is no good offering birds apple or banana skins. Finches and sparrows will eat grain or bird-seed.

Insect-eating birds are very fond of mealworms which can be bought at any pet shop. Armed with a supply of these you will have no difficulty in taming your garden robin to feed from the hand. Mealworms are not worms at all but the grubs of a beetle, and once you have acquired a stock it is easy enough to breed some more. Punch a few holes in the lid of a large tin, line the bottom with some sawdust or old rags and put the mealworms in with some bran or slices of wholemeal bread to feed on. If you allow some of the grubs to change into cream-coloured pupae and later into beetles, you will ensure a supply of future generations of mealworms.

Birds are not orderly guests; devil take the hindmost is the rule of their meals. So it is important to provide separate feeding facilities for the larger and smaller ones, especially to discourage the greedy starlings and sparrows. Tits normally feed while hanging upside-down on swaying branches, so you can help them and keep away the sparrows by hanging up their food, either as half-coconuts or in little wire baskets or 'tit cones' or on a small tray suspended from a branch or window-sill. Sometimes a particularly intelligent sparrow will learn to feed like the tits and then there is nothing much you can do except to stop feeding the tits for a few days and hope the sparrow will go elsewhere. Tits will also come with other birds to a bird-table mounted on a pole. Bird-tables are easily made at home (Fig. 66), and if you use a smooth metal pole it will stop cats, rats, and mice from climbing up. Mice can also be warded off a wooden pole by the use of a 'mouse guard' device such as is put on ships' hawsers to stop the rats from

66. Robin and blue tit at a bird-table

going ashore. A roof over the bird-table will prevent the food from getting wet and soggy in the rain. Bird-tables should not be sited too far from bushes or other cover, so that if cats or other unwelcome guests gate-crash the meal the birds can quickly dive for safety. The Royal Society for the Protection of Birds have a good selection of equipment available for feeding birds, including nut cylinders, scrap baskets, seed hoppers, tit cones, and bird tables.

Not all birds like to fly up to bird-tables to feed, so scatter some on the ground for the blackbirds, thrushes, and hedge-sparrows, but not too much or you will be feeding the mice as well. Cats, of course, should be strongly discouraged in gardens where birds are fed regularly and so should unruly dogs that bark at birds.

Almost as important as food is water, both for drinking and for bathing. An old sink or even a large frying pan, sunk in the ground, is much better than a fancy bird-bath attended by a plaster gnome. It must be shallow enough for the smaller birds

161

to be able to bathe as well as the larger ones and it should be kept clear of ice in frosty weather. The quickest way of doing this is to pour in an occasional kettle of hot water during the daytime, but some people go to the trouble of putting a candle or nightlight under an inverted flower pot with a drinking vessel on top. Do not use glycerine for this makes the water sticky and gets on to the birds' feathers when they preen.

An excellent way to help conserve bird life is to provide nestboxes in gardens and woodland. Most hole-nesting birds will nest in these, but in small gardens the most likely species are robins, great and blue tits, and spotted flycatchers. In larger and more rural gardens or in woodlands, redstarts, pied flycatchers, tree sparrows, and coal and marsh tits may be added to the list. There are basically two kinds of nestbox: an enclosed box or cylinder having a small entrance hole, which is favoured by tits, redstarts, tree sparrows, and pied flycatchers, and a less completely enclosed ledge or tray from which the sitting bird can look out, favoured by robins, pied wagtails, and spotted flycatchers. These two types are both very easily made by amateur carpenters from a piece of deal board. Many specialized nestboxes have also been designed, among them a completely unprotected flat ledge for swallows, a chimney or tunnel type for owls, an open-mouthed wicker basket for mallards, and a flattened crevice-type for tree-creepers. Further information about all these and how to make them can be found in the British Trust for Ornithology's excellent field guide on nestboxes, while the boxes themselves are obtainable from the R.S.P.B.

Nestboxes should be firmly fixed to a tree or fence so that they cannot fall down, and with an aspect that prevents the eggs being chilled by cold winds or the nestlings roasted by hot sunshine (Fig. 51). It is a good idea to fix the lid with a small hook so that it does not blow off. If the site is secure from marauders such as small boys, the nestbox can be sited low enough down to permit of the luxury of occasionally opening the lid to see what is going on inside, but this privilege should not be abused. Anybody who puts up a nestbox takes on a moral responsibility for seeing that no avoidable accident happens to the resultant brood of young birds. It is inadvisable to look into a nestbox even as often as once a day.

Sooner or later everybody is called on to handle a bird, for instance when one enters the house and has to be caught and released outside. Great care is necessary in doing this, for on the one hand the bird must be held firmly enough to stop it struggling and on the other no pressure must be exerted on its body as this may kill it. How to hold a small bird, is shown in Fig. 50. By the first method, the bird is held in one hand with its neck between the first and second fingers, and by the second it is held with its back on the palm of the hand and its head towards the holder, whose little finger is over its neck. Special care is necessary with larger birds, which can do considerable damage with both bill and feet if given the opportunity.

Perhaps the most frequent reason for handling a bird is when it is picked up sick or injured and the finder hopes to try to bring it back to health. This may be a lengthy and arduous task, and would-be good Samaritans are advised to think twice before burdening themselves with a patient who may need feeding at more frequent intervals than is convenient in the routine of a human household. Here again there is a useful B.T.O. Field Guide, on *Treatment of Sick and Wounded Birds*, from which a few very elementary hints are extracted, but which should be consulted on points of detail if an actual patient arrives on your doorstep. If a bird is weak enough to allow itself to be just picked up it is probably fairly near its end anyway, and unless it can be persuaded to eat soon it will certainly die. Soaked bread will do as emergency food for a starving insect-eating bird and birdseed for a seed-eater. Normal first-aid methods can be used to cope with flesh wounds, broken legs (if the broken part is the tarsus or lower part of the leg), and subluxation of the carpal joint, in which the wing quills are twisted outwards and should be cut off to await the next moult. Broken wings and thighs or injured beaks are much more difficult, and it is probably kinder in the long run to destroy the bird.

An all-too-frequent cause of incapacity in sea-birds is oiling, as a result of illegal disposal of oily waste from ships in the sea. Badly oiled birds are hopeless cases, but the B.T.O. Field Guide has some advice for those who are prepared to undertake the time-consuming task of rescuing slightly oiled birds (Fig. 67). These may be cleaned up by applying warm water and a detergent to the soiled plumage, the detergent being finally rinsed away with plain warm water. Some of the more badly clogged plumage may be cut away. Since this treatment completely destroys the water-proofing of the bird's plumage, it will become waterlogged and die of cold and pneumonia if it is returned to the sea. It must therefore be kept in captivity and fed fairly frequently until its next moult.

Another frequent problem is the young bird apparently deserted by its parents and brought to the local bird-lover by well-meaning small boys. The best advice is to take these

67. Badly oiled guillemot

birds straight away back to where they were found. The chances are that they have not been deserted at all, but have drawn attention to themselves by their penetrating hunger cries. Only if it is quite certain, after an hour or so's watching from a concealed position, that the parents have indeed deserted it or suffered some calamity, should anybody undertake the even more time-consuming task of rearing a fledgeling. It is well to remember that a young bird's day lasts from sunrise to sunset, and it expects to be fed at least hourly throughout this time. Insect-eating birds can be fed with the special mixture obtainable from pet shops. Young seed-eaters can be given some biscuit meal with codliver oil biscuit and a little egg. But anybody enthusiastic enough to launch into this task should certainly read the B.T.O. Field Guide first.

Further Reading

Cohen, Edwin, *Nestboxes*, B.T.O. Field Guide No. 3, 1961.

Cornwallis, R. K., and Smith, A. E., *The Bird in the Hand*, B.T.O. Field Guide No. 6, 1960.

Howard, Len, *Living with Birds*, 1956.
    Birds as Individuals, 1952.

Knight, Maxwell, *Bird Gardening*, 1954.

Lake, F. B., *Treatment of Sick and Wounded Birds*, B.T.O. Field Guide No. 5, 1960.

Appendix and Index

Appendix: Natural History Societies

Permanent addresses only are given, as so many societies' addresses change with a new secretary. For the current address of any society whose address is not listed below, apply to the Intelligence Unit, Council for Nature, 41 Queen's Gate, London SW7. Membership of the Council for Nature is given as in October 1962. The Council has members in Northern Ireland and the Channel Isles but not in Eire.

National Natural History Societies
(Members of the Council for Nature)

Amateur Entomologists' Society, 1 West Ham Lane, London E15.

Army Bird Watching Society

Association for the Study of Animal Behaviour

Association of School Natural History Societies

Botanical Society of the British Isles, c/o Dept of Botany, British Museum (Natural History), London SW7.

British Bryological Society

British Ecological Society

British Herpetological Society, c/o Zoological Society of London, Regent's Park, London NW1.

British Junior Naturalists' Association, c/o The Museum, Scarborough, Yorks.

British Lichen Society

British Mycological Society

British Naturalists' Association

British Ornithologists' Union, c/o The Bird Room, British Museum (Natural History), London SW7.

British Phycological Society, Marine Station, Millport, Isle of Cumbrae, Scotland.

British Pteridological Society

British Trust for Entomology, 41 Queen's Gate, London SW7.
British Trust for Ornithology, 2 King Edward Street, Oxford.

Cave Research Group of Great Britain
Conchological Society of Great Britain and Ireland, c/o British
    Museum (Natural History), London SW7.

Fauna Preservation Society, c/o Zoological Society of London,
    Regent's Park, London NW1.
Field Studies Council, 9 Devereux Court, Strand, London WC2.
Freshwater Biological Association, The Ferry House, Far Sawrey,
    Ambleside, Westmorland.

Institute of Biology, 41 Queen's Gate, London SW7.

Linnean Society of London, Burlington House, Piccadilly,
    London W1.

Mammal Society of the British Isles, c/o Institute of Biology, 41
    Queen's Gate, London SW7.
Marine Biological Association of the United Kingdom, The
    Laboratory, Citadel Hill, Plymouth, Devon.

Nature Cine Club

Quekett Microscopical Club, c/o The Royal Society, Burlington
    House, Piccadilly, London W1.

Romany Society
Royal Entomological Society, 41 Queen's Gate, London SW7.
Royal Naval Bird Watching Society
Royal Society for the Protection of Birds, The Lodge, Sandy,
    Beds.

School Natural Science Society
Scottish Field Studies Association
Scottish Marine Biological Association, Marine Station, Mill-
    port, Isle of Cumbrae, Scotland.
Scottish Ornithologists' Club, 21 Regent Terrace, Edinburgh 7.
Selborne Society
Society for the Promotion of Nature Reserves, c/o British
    Museum (Natural History), London SW7.

Wildfowl Trust, New Grounds, Slimbridge, Gloucestershire.

Zoological Photographic Club
Zoological Society of London, Regent's Park, London NW1.

Local Natural History Societies

*(Members of the Council for Nature; omitting naturalists' trusts
and bird observatories, which are listed separately)*

Altrincham and District Natural History Society
Ambleside Field Society
Andersonian Naturalists of Glasgow
Armagh Field Naturalists' Society
Ashmolean Natural History Society of Oxfordshire

Bacup Natural History Society
Banbury Ornithological Society
Banffshire Society
Barnsley Naturalist and Scientific Society
Barrow Naturalists' Field Club
Batley Natural History Society
Bedfordshire Natural History Society and Field Club
Belfast Natural History and Philosophical Society
Belfast Naturalists' Field Club
Bexhill Museum Association
Birmingham Natural History and Philosophical Society
Blackburn Naturalists' Field Club
Botanical Society of Edinburgh
Bournemouth Natural Science Society
Brighton and Hove Natural History Society
Bristol Naturalists' Society
Brixham Museum and History Society
Buckinghamshire Archaeological Society
Burton on Trent Natural History and Archaeological Society
Bury St Edmunds and District Naturalists' Society
Buxton Archaeological and Natural History Society
Buxton Field Club

Camberley Natural History Society
Camborne and Redruth Natural History Society

Cambridge Bird Club
Cambridge Natural History Society
Cardiff Naturalists' Society
Castleford and District Naturalists' Society
Chester Society of Natural Science, Literature and Art
Cleveland Naturalists' Field Club
Clitheroe Naturalists' Society
Colchester Natural History Society and Field Club
Collingham and District Bird Watching Group
Colne Naturalists' Society
Colne Valley Ornithological Society
Colworth Natural History Society
Consett and District Naturalists' Field Club
Cornwall Bird Watching and Preservation Society
Cotteswold Naturalists' Field Club
Coventry and District Natural History and Scientific Society
Craven Naturalists' and Scientific Association
Crawley Field Club
Cross Hill Naturalists' Society
Croydon Natural History and Scientific Society

Darlington and Teesdale Naturalists' Field Club
Derby Natural History Society
Derbyshire Entomological Society
Derbyshire Ornithological Society
Devon Bird Watching and Preservation Society
Devonshire Association for the Advancement of Science
Doncaster Naturalists' Society
Doncaster and District Ornithological Society
Dorset Field Ornithology Group
Dorset Natural History and Archaeological Society
Dover and Deal Natural History Society
Dumfriesshire and Galloway Natural History and Antiquarian
    Society
Dundee Naturalists' Society
Dunfermline Naturalists' Society
Dursley and District Bird Watching and Preservation Society
Dyserth and District Field Club

East Grinstead and District Natural Science Society

East Lancashire Ornithologists' Club
Eden Field Club
Edinburgh Natural History Society
Essex Bird Watching and Preservation Society
Essex Field Club
Exeter Natural History Society

Farnborough Natural History Society
Flintshire Ornithological Society
Folkestone Natural History Society

Gower Ornithological Society
Grange and District Natural History Society
Guildford Natural History and Literary Society

Halifax Scientific Society
Hamilton Natural History Group
Hampshire Field Club and Archaeological Society
Hampstead Heath and Old Hampstead Protection Society
Hampstead Scientific Society
Haslemere Natural History Society
Hastings Natural History Society
Hayes and Harlington Natural History and Antiquarian Society
Herefordshire Ornithological Club
Hertfordshire Natural History Society and Field Club
Horsham Natural History Society
Huntingdonshire Fauna and Flora Society

Inverness Botany Group
Inverness Scientific Society and Field Club
Ipswich and District Natural History Society
Isle of Man Natural History and Antiquarian Society
Isle of Wight Natural History and Archaeological Society

Kendal Natural History Society
Kent Field Club
Kent Ornithological Society
Kilmarnock Glenfield Ramblers
Kirkcaldy Naturalists' Society

Lancaster and District Bird Watching Society
Leeds Co-operative Naturalists' Field Club
Leeds and District Bird Watchers' Club

Leeds Philosophical and Literary Society
Leek and District Field Club
Leicester Literary and Philosophical Society
Leicestershire and Rutland Ornithological Society
Letchworth Naturalists' Society
Lincolnshire Naturalists' Union
Littlehampton Natural Science and Archaeology Society
Liverpool Botanical Society
Liverpool Teachers' Nature Study Group
Lizard Field Club
London Natural History Society
Long Ashton Research Station Recreational Club – Natural
    History Section
Loughborough Naturalists' Club
Louth Naturalists' Antiquarian and Literary Society
Lowestoft and North Suffolk Field Naturalists' Club
Lymington and District Naturalists' Society

Macclesfield and District Field Club
Malvern Field Club
Manchester Entomological Society
Manchester Ornithological Society
Merseyside Naturalists' Association
Mid-Argyll Natural History and Antiquarian Society
Middle Thames Natural History Society
Mid-Somerset Naturalists' Society
Mirfield Naturalists' Society
Monmouth and District Field and Antiquarian Society
Montgomeryshire Field Society

Nelson Natural History Society
New Forest Ornithologists' Club
Newbury District Ornithological Club
Newcastle-under-Lyme Natural History Society
Norfolk and Norwich Naturalists' Society
Norfolk Research Committee
North East Essex Educational Fellowship, Field Studies Group
North East Lancashire Naturalists' Union
North Gloucestershire Naturalists' Society
North Staffordshire Field Club

North Western Naturalists' Union
Northamptonshire Natural History Society and Field Club
Northern Naturalists' Club
Northumberland, Durham, and Newcastle upon Tyne Natural
  History Society
Nottingham Natural Science Field Club

Oldham Microscopical Society and Field Club
Oldham Natural History Society
Orkney Field Club
Orpington Field Club
Oxford Ornithological Society

Penrith and District Natural History Society
Perthshire Society of Natural Science
Peterborough Museum Society
Poole and District Natural History Society
Portsmouth and District Natural History Society
Preston Scientific Society
Purbeck Society

Reading Natural History Society
Reading Ornithological Club
Royal Geological Society of Cornwall
Royal Institution of South Wales
Rugby Natural History Society
Ruislip and District Natural History Society
Rye Natural History Society

St Osyth Bird Watching and Protection Society
Salisbury and District Natural History Society
Scarborough Field Naturalists' Society
Seaford Natural History Society
Shoreham Ornithological Society
Shropshire Ornithological Society
Société Guernesiaise
Somerset Archaeological and Natural History Society
Somerset Archaeological and Natural History Society – Ornitho-
  logical Section
Sorby Natural History Society
South Eastern Union of Scientific Societies

South Essex Natural History Society
South London Botanical Institute
South London Entomological and Natural History Society
South Western Naturalists' Union
Southampton Natural History Society
Steep Holm Trust
Stowmarket and District Naturalists' Society
Suffolk Naturalists' Society
Surbiton and District Bird Watching Society
Surrey Bird Club
Sussex Ornithological Society
Sutton Coldfield Natural History Society

Todmorden Natural History Society
Torquay Natural History Society
Trent Valley Bird Watchers
Tunbridge Wells Natural History and Philosophical Society

Ulster Society for the Protection of Birds
United Field Naturalists' Society, Manchester

Wakefield Naturalists' Society
Wantage and District Field Club
Warrington Field Club and Scientific Society
Warwick Natural History Society
West Midland Bird Club
Weybridge Natural History and Aquarist Society
Wharfedale Naturalists' Society
Wigan and District Field Club
Wiltshire Archaeological and Natural History Society
Worcestershire Naturalists' Club
Worthing Natural History Society

Yorkshire Naturalists' Union
Yorkshire Philosophical Society

County Naturalists' Trusts

(*An asterisk indicates a member of Council for Nature*)

Bedfordshire and Huntingdonshire Naturalists' Trust

*Berkshire, Buckinghamshire, and Oxfordshire Naturalists' Trust

*Cambridgeshire and Isle of Ely Naturalists' Trust
 Cheshire Conservation Trust

 Derbyshire Naturalists' Trust
*Devon Naturalists' Trust
*Dorset Naturalists' Trust

*Essex Naturalists' Trust

*Glamorgan County Naturalists' Trust
*Gloucestershire Trust for Nature Conservation

*Hampshire and Isle of Wight Naturalists' Trust
 Herefordshire and Radnorshire Nature Trust

*Kent Naturalists' Trust

 Lake District Naturalists' Trust
 Lancashire Naturalists' Trust
*Leicestershire Trust for Nature Conservation
*Lincolnshire Naturalists' Trust

*Norfolk Naturalists' Trust
 Northumberland and Durham Naturalists' Trust

 Suffolk Naturalists' Trust
*Surrey Naturalists' Trust
*Sussex Naturalists' Trust

*West Midlands Nature Conservation Trust
*West Wales Naturalists' Trust
 Wiltshire Trust for Nature Conservation

*Yorkshire Naturalists' Trust

Bird and Field Observatories

(*An asterisk indicates a member of Council for Nature*)

*Bardsey Bird and Field Observatory, Aberdaron, North Wales.
 Bradwell Bird Observatory, Bradwell-on-Sea, Essex.

 Calf of Man Bird Observatory, Isle of Man.
 Cape Clear Bird Observatory, Skibbereen, County Cork, Eire.
*Cley Bird Observatory, Holt, Norfolk.
*Copeland Bird Observatory, via Belfast, Northern Ireland.

*Dungeness Bird Observatory, Romney Marsh, Kent.

*Fair Isle Bird Observatory, Shetland.

Gibraltar Point Bird Observatory and Field Study Centre, Skegness, Lincs. (*Lincolnshire Naturalists' Trust.)

Isle of May Bird Observatory and Field Station, Fife.

Jersey Bird Observatory, St Ouen's Nature Reserve, Jersey, C.I.

Lundy Field Station and Observatory, via Bideford, Devon. (*Lundy Field Society.)

New Grounds, Slimbridge, Gloucestershire. (*Wildfowl Trust.)

*Portland Bird Observatory and Field Centre, Portland Bill, Dorset.

Rathlin Island Bird Observatory, Ballycastle, County Antrim, Northern Ireland.

St Agnes Bird Observatory, Isles of Scilly.
Saltee Bird Observatory, County Wexford, Eire.
Sandwich Bay Bird Observatory, Kent.
Skokholm Bird Observatory, Dale, Haverfordwest, Pembrokeshire. (*Field Studies Council.)
Spurn Bird Observatory, Kilnsea, Yorks.

Tory Island Bird Observatory, County Donegal, Eire.

Walberswick Bird Observatory, Suffolk.

For information about how to stay at these observatories, apply to the British Trust for Ornithology.

Field Centres

Brantwood Conference and Holiday Centre. (Council for Nature.)

Dale Fort Field Centre, Haverfordwest, Pembrokeshire. (Field Studies Council.)

Flatford Mill Field Centre, East Bergholt, Colchester, Essex. (Field Studies Council.)

Garth Memorial Youth Hostel, Fortingall, Aberfeldy, Perthshire. (Scottish Field Studies Association.)

Hutton Buscel Field Study Centre, Scarborough. (British Junior Naturalists' Association.)

Juniper Hall Field Centre, Dorking, Surrey. (Field Studies Council.)

Malham Tarn Field Centre, Settle, Yorkshire. (Field Studies Council.)

Preston Montford Field Centre, Shrewsbury, Salop. (Field Studies Council.)

Slapton Ley Field Centre, Slapton, Kingsbridge, Devon. (Field Studies Council.)

School, College, and Young People's Societies

(*Members of the Council for Nature*)

Allhallows School Natural History Society

Bembridge School Natural History Society

Field Observers' Club

Henley Grammar School Field Club
Houghton Mill Youth Hostel

Isleworth Polytechnic

Junior Naturalists' Club

King's College Natural History Society, Newcastle

London University Natural History Society

Mid-Somerset Naturalists' Society (Junior Section)
Mill Hill School Natural History Society

Newton Park College
Notre Dame Field Studies Association

Ranelagh School Out of Doors Club
Royal College of Science Natural History Society

Stranmillis College Field Study Society

Tonbridge School Natural History Society

University College of Swansea Field Society

XYZ Club, c/o Zoological Society of London, Regent's Park, London, N W I.

Museums in Membership of the Council for Nature

Aberdeen Art Gallery

Birmingham City Museum and Art Gallery
Bolton Museum and Art Gallery
Bristol City Museum

Carlisle Public Library, Museum and Art Gallery
Curtis Museum, Alton

Doncaster Museum and Art Gallery

Glasgow Art Gallery and Museum

Hancock Museum, Newcastle upon Tyne
Haslemere Educational Museum
Herbert Art Gallery and Museum

Ipswich Museums

City of Leicester Museums
Lincoln City and County Museum

Paisley Museum and Art Galleries

Reading Museum and Art Gallery

St Albans City Museum
Scarborough Museum of Natural History
Sunderland Museum and Art Gallery

Ulster Museum

Wollaton Hall Natural History Museum

Universities in Membership of the Council for Nature

Birmingham University, Botany Department
Birmingham University, Zoology Department

Hull University, Botany Department
Hull University, Zoology Department

London University, King's College

St Andrews University

Other Bodies in Membership of the Council for Nature
(*Excepting Museums and Universities*)

B.B.C. Natural History Unit, Broadcasting House, Whiteladies Road, Bristol, 8.

Climbers' Club

Council for the Preservation of Rural England, 4 Hobart Place, London sw1.

Council for the Preservation of Rural Wales, 4 Hobart Place, London sw1.

Dartmoor Preservation Association

Exmoor Society

Flyfishers' Club, 3 Whitehall Court, London, sw1.

Glasgow Tree Lovers' Society
Gower Society

Henry Doubleday Research Association

Herbert Whitley Trust, Primley Estate Office, 190 Totnes Road, Paignton, Devon.

Holiday Fellowship, Fellowship House, 142 Great North Way, Hendon, London NW4.

Men of the Trees

National Federation of Young Farmers' Clubs, 55 Gower Street, London wc1.

Ramblers' Association, 48 Park Road, Baker Street, London NW1.

Universities Federation for Animal Welfare, 7a Lamb's Conduit Passage, London wc1.

Youth Hostels Association, Trevelyan House, St Albans, Herts.

Index